THE SCHOONER THAT CAME HOME
The Final Voyage of the C. A. THAYER

THE
SCHOONER
THAT CAME
HOME

THE FINAL

VOYAGE OF THE *C. A. THAYER*

By HARLAN TROTT

CORNELL MARITIME PRESS

Cambridge, Maryland 1958

Manufactured in the United States of America

For Eleanor, Stephen and Ian

Acknowledgments

Some of the record relating to the *C. A. Thayer's* last passage was extracted from the schooner's official logbook, and later was interwoven in a descriptive summary of the voyage appearing in *The Christian Science Monitor*. My thanks to the *Monitor*, and to The MacMillan Company of New York for permission to quote verses from their 1935 edition of "Poems" by Sir John Masefield.

I am indebted to the late Capt. Ole Lee, onetime Coast Pilot for the Waterman Steamship Company; Mr. Gus Carlson, Mrs. Peter Nelson and Mr. John A. Mackrodt for information about their earlier experiences in the *C. A. Thayer*. Also to Mr. Johnnie Gruelund, Chief Rigger of the ship *Balclutha*, for his translations from the Danish of Sophus Hartwick's: "Danes in Early California Shipping;" Mr. David Nelson and Mr. Roger Olmstead of the San Francisco Maritime Museum staff, and Mr. Harold Huycke for their generous assistance. Some information relating to Alaska salmon salting is the result of Mr. Olmstead's special research in Bancroft Library.

And finally my very special thanks to Director Karl Kortum of the San Francisco Maritime Museum for placing his photographs of the *C. A. Thayer* at my disposal and for combing the manuscript for mistakes, and to that eminent maritime historian Dr. John Lyman for his original research in helping to con the book's final course.

Foreword

The sailing ship has been badly neglected by the professional historian, and most of the works on the history of sailing ships have been produced as a sideline by those who must earn their living in other ways. This book tells of a two-week voyage made by a group of such enthusiasts in the course of moving one of the last surviving lumber schooners of the Pacific Coast from Puget Sound, where she was suffering the ignominious fate of posing as the "pirate ship" *Black Shield*, to San Francisco, her first home port, where preservation as an authentic link with the past awaited her under the auspices of the State of California at the urging of the San Francisco Maritime Museum.

Harlan Trott has skillfully interwoven his account of the *C. A. Thayer's* final voyage, illustrated with Karl Kortum's photographs, with the highlights of her past history. The *C. A. Thayer* was but one of over 400 sailing vessels built on the Pacific Coast between 1860 and 1905 to carry fir and redwood lumber from the tidewater mills of Washington, Oregon, and Northern California to market. The larger vessels, barkentines and four- or even five-masted schooners, often went offshore to Hawaii, Australia, China, or the West Coast of South America. Some even went to South Africa, a voyage that took them all the way around the world. The two-masters and baldheaded three-masters were primarily coasters, designed to run to San Francisco, Southern California, or to Mexican ports of the Gulf of California and as far south as Acapulco, and to return empty to the mill ports.

The Pacific Coast produces no oak or other hardwood timber worth mentioning, and it took time for the inherent prejudices of shipping people against "softwood" in hull construction to be overcome. However, by the time the *C.A. Thayer* was built, the full qualities of Douglas fir as a shipbuilding material were recognized, and the lumber carriers were fashioned entirely of this timber: keel and keelson, stempost and sternpost, floors and frames, knees, planking and ceiling, decks, masts, and spars. Only in the treenails, which were commonly imported Eastern locust; in the corners of the bitts, which were often of mesquite from the Arizona desert; and in the gaff and boom jaws, the cleats and cavils, and the pinrails were hardwoods used.

Toward the southern part of its range, in Northern California, the Douglas fir does not grow in the pure, dense stands that characterize its distribution in Oregon and Washington. Known to the California shipbuilders as Humboldt Pine, these random fir trees grew large and tall in various sections of the redwood forests. The 19th century lumbermen of Northern California, who were primarily engaged in manufacturing redwood lumber, were happy to supply shipbuilders with all the Douglas fir logs they could use. A compatriot of Hans Bendixsen named Thomas H. Peterson was engaged for nearly twenty years in converting the fir timber of the Mendocino coast into seagoing schooners, floating two- and three-masters at places where today it is hard to imagine a dory being launched.

Most lumber companies of the last century operated on a shoestring capital, and although the *Thayer* was operated by the E. K. Wood Lumber Company, that firm actually owned only a sixteenth interest in her, representing an investment of less than $2,000. Bendixsen, her builder, owned a full quarter of her, which must have represented an investment of cash on his part as well as profit, for, as the appendix shows, he usually invested in only an eighth or sixteenth of his products. Captain C. W. Liljeqvist, the *Thayer's* first master, owned a sixteenth, and the rest was distributed among 13 other part-owners, mainly in San Francisco, whose individual shares ranged down to a sixty-fourth. Under this type of financing, the E. K. Wood Lumber Company as shippers formally chartered the vessel from the E. K. Wood Lumber Company as managing owners at the prevailing market rates before each cargo was loaded, paying a stipulated freight rate per thousand board feet of lumber carried. The managing owners collected the freight money from themselves, paid the schooner's expenses, which included a commission on their collections or disbursements, and distributed the profits regularly to the part-owners.

By managing a fleet of such schooners, a lumber company was assured a steady supply of tonnage to carry its products from its mills in the north to its lumber yards in California, at the same time reducing to a minimum its capital requirement. About the time the *C. A. Thayer* was built, however, a new type of transportation, financed in a new way, was appearing on the scene. This was the steam schooner, a somewhat misnamed type, since it was mostly steamer and very little schooner. Having an engine, it could operate on a predictable schedule not subject to the whims of the wind, and thus it could be chartered by the month rather than by the trip. Likewise it could visit several mills along a river to load and could discharge at several different wharves or even ports without running up ruinous towing bills. And since the lumber yards it served could order small consignments at frequent intervals instead of cargo lots, they could operate with a smaller inventory, knowing that a telegraph order to the mill would be delivered in a week or ten days.

Thus by 1900 the coasting lumber trade was passing to the steam schooners, which were largely financed as single-ship corporations with most of the capital obtained as bank loans secured against long-term time charters from the mills. More and more of the sailing schooners were either going offshore or were cutting rates (and dividends). Between 1895 and 1903, the *C. A. Thayer* made six foreign voyages, probably mostly to Mexican ports, which were unattractive for the steam schooners, but on the last of these she went to Fiji, going down from Grays Harbor in the good time of 38 days.

Peter M. Nelson bought up all the *Thayer's* shares in 1912, and the part-owners were doubtless happy to recover most of their investment from a concern whose future seemed so doubtful. Who in 1912 could look ahead to World War I and the inflated freight rates of 1917-20? Nelson used the *Thayer* every summer through 1924 in his Bristol Bay salmon-salting business, squeezing in Australian voyages in some of the winters, when return cargoes of copra were available. In April 1925 the Pacific Coast Codfish Company of Seattle bought the schooner, and, except for World War II service as a barge, she spent most of the next 25 years in summer voyages to the Bering Sea, where cod were caught from dories and salted in the hold. In October 1954 she was acquired by Charles McNeal of North Lilliwaup, Washington, from whom the State of California bought her in June 1957.

The people of San Francisco are fortunate in having among them the public-spirited group who have had both the vision to create an authentic record of the city's maritime history and the energy to carry the project through to completion. The voyage described in this book added to that history while preserving it.

John Lyman

Preface

This is the log of the *C. A. Thayer* and of an epic kind of adventure that marks the last voyage of the last West Coast lumber schooner.

In a way, too, it is a sentimental story interwoven with a thin gold thread of retrospect, of personal recollections about a wind-driven ship and a way of life as old as time—as enduring and yet as illusive.

The *C. A. Thayer's* final voyage from Seattle to San Francisco is significant in that it symbolizes, at least on the Pacific Coast, the end of an era of maritime trade and travel in a world now ured in terms of time—of hours and minutes from departure to landfall instead of interminable, sea-tossed distances.

In a sense, also, this is an "official" record of the last voyage of the last of the small fore-and-aft rigged vessels on which the greater part of the American west coast's domestic trade was bottomed for a long time. This is the way it unfolded, in an alternately slow and swift montage of calm and storm, but frequently in spells of dreary drifting in the tranquil old rote of sail Joseph Conrad described as the "magic monotony of existence between sky and water."

Long after our civilization had put its roots down in these red-rock cliffs, the sea was still the easiest and the most efficient means of communication between the cities of California and the Pacific Northwest. When the *C. A. Thayer* was launched in 1895, the greater bulk of north-south commerce still moved by sea.

Then, as railroads and highways ate into this free flow of domestic trade, the schooners were driven off. Most of them vanished in the natural attrition of winter tempests that assail this bold Pacific shoreline. A few of them hazarded long transpacific passages, or drifted into the Bering Sea cod and salmon salteries. The *C. A. Thayer* essayed them all and held out to the last.

No fast sail passages splash the record of this invincible old timber drougher. No swashbuckling mutinies color her prosaic career. The *C. A. Thayer* asserts no special claim to glory. If an old ship could talk, perhaps she could only paraphrase the thought expressed by the Frenchman Talleyrand who, when asked what he had done for his country in the Revolution, replied, "I survived, didn't I?"

This is good enough for the history-minded men of California, the civic leaders who said the *C. A. Thayer* belongs in the State's maritime historical museum, to be kept there in trust so that the future may see and feel under its feet the tall, square-timbered integrity out of which this era was shaped.

Harlan Trott

Walnut Creek, California

Table of Contents

Vessels built by H. D. Bendixsen on Humboldt Bay.

". . . Vell, in the *Thayer*, ve had to go this vay, and that vay, and
that vay, and that vay . . . and sometimes, ve couldn't go at all . . . .
They call it, 'Heave to'. . . . . . "

Chapter I

The Builder

Our leave-taking is like the send-offs Nantucket gave her Swains and Starbucks in the heigh-old days of Downeast whaling. Families and friends in their Sunday finery flood the excited pierhead scene. And sentimental shellbacks have turned out in droves to see the schooner sail.

Yachts glisten in the offing. Newsreel cameras crank in the drama of the old windjammer's leavetaking, as the tugboat *Trojan* pushes her manila bow fender in to the *C. A. Thayer's* stout wooden planks.

We are victualed and iced down for fourteen days. But there is cheerful talk about making it in five. The record is said to be three days and fourteen hours, Umpqua River to the San Pedro Breakwater, made by her Bendixsen-built sister, the Knowland schooner, *Sadie*. This record course is a little longer than the rhumb-line distance the captain's dividers would lay off on the chart from Cape Flattery to the Farallones.

But who knows? Give us a fair wind out of the cold North Pacific and our high, unballasted ship may write a new record into the history of fast sail passages from Flattery to the Golden Gate.

And there are extra hands to make quick and light work of ship handling if Capt. Adrian Raynaud and his two mates in the after-house are more than half a mind to drive her.

Deep down in the eyes of her, our big Bering Sea fishermen's fo'c's'le is swarming with brawny zeal. In her timber-coasting days, four able seamen berthed in the forward house were all it took to work her. We are fifteen forward, counting the two super-numeraries, Steve Wilson of Port Blakely, a photographer-naturalist and me.

1

Along Seattle's Waterfront . . . The greater part of the crew came up from San Francisco for the *Thayer's* last voyage.

Right off Pan American's new Artic clipper from London, I am the last aboard, an hour before the turn of the tide—toting a borrowed bedroll and some undersized storm gear, rustled up in a breathless pierhead phone call to a Seattle newspaper colleague.

The schooner's three sturdy new masts are swimming like a row of Christopher Wren steeples in the warm autumn sunshine, and the new hemp cordage is making gull noises in the white-painted blocks, straining to be off on the high water. Outboard, the sun glints on the fresh paintwork, half hiding the old girl's 62 years.

"All ashore that are going ashore!" The ladder is dragged in. Cook Clark Turner has said his farewells. Already the Charley Noble on his galley house is wafting out the hearty portents of supper. The deputy fire marshal of Everett, Washington, is destined to play a big role on this voyage. The sea cook is a key man, the first and the last on the job of appeasing this hungry horde.

After 62 years of West Coast timber droughing, deep-sea trading and Arctic fishing, the *C. A. Thayer* is bound away for San Francisco to live on and on in the State maritime museum's windjammers' Valhalla.

The *Thayer* is what they call a baldheaded schooner measuring 156 feet from stem post to rudder post, 36 feet through the beam and 11 feet, 10 inches deep in the hold. Counting her deckload, the schooner could stow 575,000 board feet of lumber. She was built for E. K. Wood Lumber Company and named for one of the firm's partners.

A contemporary of Clarence A. Thayer's son remembers the elder Thayer as a serious strait-laced businessman, as "stiff and unbending" as the schooner's three great Oregon fir masts. As the public property of California's state park sytem, she is destined to long outlive her namesake's fame.

Last of the three-masted schooners that loaded lumber in the North Pacific ports for San Francisco and southern California, the *C. A. Thayer* has two Australian voyages in her record. During World War II she was an unrigged Navy barge. And as late as 1956, she was earning money in the weird masquerade of a tourist "pirate ship" on the evergreen slopes of Hood's Canal near the little Washington State village of Lilliwaup North.

A look at their handiwork . . . The mate and John Davies stroll along Seattle's Alaskan Way after a dinner of halibut cheeks.

The *C. A. Thayer* was built at Fairhaven, California, in 1895, by the master builder, H. D. Bendixsen. His fame as an early California shipwright took sturdy root in the easy lines and oak-ribbed integrity of the first few small vessels he built on his own.

The man who built her . . . Capt. Hans Bendixsen.

Hans Ditlev Bendixsen was born at Thisted, Denmark, in 1842; found the feel of a shipwright's tools at Poul Pagh's yard in Aalborg and later at Jacob Holm's and Poap & Mitchelsen's ship ways in the beautiful city of Copenhagen.

The story of his life merits some reflection. For, if as they say, a man is in his work, then surely it must explain and verify the hard, sea-tested values in the vessels he built, vessels such as his *C. A. Thayer*. Hans Bendixsen's practical knowledge, his fine-edged skill, his unstinted labor and his honesty gained him a handsome living and some renown wherever Bendixsen ships were mentioned.

Joining her.

All this must have been latent in the purposefulness of Thisted's shipwright's apprentice who sailed out of Copenhagen as a ship's carpenter about the time of the American Civil War. Early California records show that he came to San Francisco on a voyage from Brazil and worked in the city's shipyards in the 'Sixties. Eventually, he went to Eureka to work in the E. and H. Cousins yard.

Soon, Hans Bendixsen had a yard of his own at the foot of L Street where he built his first ship, the little topmast schooner, *Fairy Queen*. Then came the *Undine*, the *Silva*, the *Elvenia*, the *Mary*, the *Humboldt*, the *Aurora*, and a host of others.

Before very long, Bendixsen outgrew the L Street yard and moved to Fairhaven on the peninsula across from Eureka. Some years there were damaging floods, and at one time fire reduced his Fairhaven yard to ashes. Hans Bendixsen lost all his timber, shipways, machinery, forge, spar loft, along with a vessel framed out in the stocks—everything except his indefatigable Danish pluck. In a few years, the Bendixsen yard was going again, full blast and debt free. Spread out over fourteen acres were shops, sawmills, slips, timber yards, even cottages and gardens for 150 workers. It was a small town.

The year he moved to Fairhaven, Bendixsen launched seven vessels, including three schooners for the South Sea Island trade. The three-mast schooner, *Compeer*, launched in 1877, was his largest up to that time. In 1883, West Coast seamen were pointing to a beautiful new white three-masted barkentine, the *City of Papeete*, and saying proudly, "There goes a Bendixsen ship."

Usually, Hans Bendixsen owned shares in Bendixsen-built ships —vessels plying the coast with lumber or trading out to the sugar islands. He held a number of shares in the 1,100-ton steamer *Humboldt*, built the year after he launched the *C. A. Thayer*. Another durable Bendixsen schooner, the famous three-master, *Wawona*, like the *C. A. Thayer*, was still at sea after World War II.

The year the *Maine* blew up in Havana Harbor was a memorable year in Fairhaven also. A group of San Franciscans headed by James H. Bruce had just commissioned their Fairhaven friend to build them a new vessel. It was a gala day at Fairhaven when the four-master *H. D. Bendixsen* slid down the ways, for she was also Bendixsen's 100th ship. Later a couple of retired Danish captains, Jens Eschen and Rasmus Minor, managed the *H. D. Bendixsen* as a side-line to their stevedoring business. As late as 1923, she was trading in the Arctic. The next year, the *H. D. Bendixsen* was lost on Point Barrow.

A decade after the gold spike was driven home at Promontory Point across the mountains, a young writer named Robert Louis Stevenson was rubbing patched elbows with immigrant hordes pouring into California over the new transcontinental cinder trails.

Scandinavians, Danes especially—bringing their maritime skills —wet their whistles on San Francisco's East Street, then made tracks for Fairhaven, lured by the shipbuilding fame of Thisted's H. D. Bendixsen.

He was good to his men. When the Danish fraternity, "Dania," held its convention at Ferndale, just south of Eureka, in February, 1900, the shipbuilder held open house at Fairhaven. That night, when Bendixsen workers knocked off too late to catch the train, the big-hearted boss chartered a special train to transport them to the Danish fete at Ferndale.

Later that same year, his health failing, Bendixsen sold the shipyard at Fairhaven. A stock company was formed to buy him out; later the yard was leased to the Hammond Lumber Company. Early in World War I, the shipyard passed into the hands of Governor James Rolph, Jr., head of a famous California shipping house. Rolph's flamboyant new broom swept away the town's transplanted New England name. Fairhaven became Rolph. In the first year alone, four wooden ocean steamers and three big offshore barkentines were launched. Orders came from France for three steamers for the North African trade. Out of such modest beginnings as Hans Bendixsen's little topsail river schooner, *Fairy Queen*, were these vast works made.

When news of Hans Ditlev Bendixsen's death spread out along the Pacific West Coast in 1902, shops closed their shutters in Fairhaven and Eureka, and all up and down the long coast the ocean flags of Matson, J. D. Spreckels, E. K. Wood, Eschen & Minor, Rolph, Charles Nelson and A. P. Lorentzen were lowered to half mast in tribute to this invincible Dane.

John A. Mackrodt, an old Cape Horn veteran of Ferdinand Laeisz's Flying "P" line of Hamburg nitrate clippers, remembers Hans Bendixsen's wife, Emma, as a dainty little German woman, erect and spirited, even when she was well past ninety.

The Mackrodts lived across the street in Alameda from Emma, who, after her second marriage, liked to be addressed as Mrs. Bendixsen-Jensen.

Emma was a sharp whist player, and John Mackrodt was her favorite partner. In 1908, Mackrodt had paid off from the barkentine, S. N. Castle, at Gray's Harbor and shipped down to San Francisco in the lumber-laden C. A. Thayer. Emma Bendixsen-Jensen was naturally sentimental. This ten-day interlude in the life of a deepwater wanderer, this brief connection with one of Hans Bendixsen's vessels, made John Mackrodt a welcome neighbor.

Emma's evening whist parties were times for reminiscing about the Thayer and the other Bendixsen ships whose oil portraits adorned Emma Bendixsen-Jensen's big parlor. Sometimes Emma would send her maid up to Park Street for a cake, and there would be references to the old times at Fairhaven when dainty little Emma rowed across Humboldt Bay to Eureka in a skiff and shopped for vegetables and stew meat to feed the hungry shipwrights and caulkers in her husband's shipyard.

In these later years, there was a cook and maid to help run the Alameda house, and an electric coupe which Emma steered with a tiller. And there was Polly, a suspicious and irascible parrot that sat on little Emma's shoulder during strolls down Pacific Street. Polly took a shine to Mackrodt who took the bird on occasional walks in the park, which pleased Emma, too. Thus, it was only natural that Emma Bendixsen-Jensen sent for John Mackrodt's wife one day to witness her signature to her will.

Emma passed on in her 102nd year, leaving her estate to charitable institutions in Hans Bendixsen's native Denmark.

When the E. K. Wood Lumber Company went to Fairhaven in 1895 for a schooner to be built to their account and to be named for their partner, C. A. Thayer, the Fairhaven shipbuilder could never have guessed what glamorous destiny lay ahead for this plain workaday ship. Little did he know that in her sturdy pine workmanship the blossom of his fame was blown.

This is the account of Hans Ditlev Bendixsen's enduring artistry. This is the story of the Fairhaven schooner's last voyage—her passage to posterity.

And now the tide is standing.
The towboat toots impatiently.
"Single up, fore and aft! Stand by to take the tug's hawser!" Commands float forward. "Let go everything!"

"Let's keep it as far from the iron wheel as possible" . . . The compass adjustor arrives just before sailing.

Chief Mate John Dickerhoff takes charge on the fo'c's'le head; suddenly his husky voice is all business. "Look alive, there! Through the chock there. Through that chock! Up here with that chafing gear! Let's have some rope yarns! Around the bitt, now, some more turns! Give us some slack! Give us some slack! Come on! Come on! What d'ya think this is, a Sunday picnic? Somebody's paying for that towboat."

The pier drifts away as the *Trojan* backs down in her own wheel wash. The mate's voice has subsided now into a nice reassuring snarl. "On deck, now, all hands! Get this mess squared away."

Families and friends . . . The pierhead scene on sailing day.

The *C. A. Thayer* is outward bound.
And on the land,
    . . . the men beholding knew
    A queen the more was passing, seeing you.

Chapter II

Giving Shape to a Dream

There's a long night's towing between the schooner *C. A. Thayer* and the great ocean swells of the north Pacific.

This is the traditional way of sailing ships going to sea from Seattle. Many a tall windjammer has passed out Puget Sound bound for Cape Horn, deep with wheat from the high plains of eastern Washington to put bread in Europe's mouth, or coastwise out with coal and lumber for the western world.

However much we admire the sweeping march of our mechanic arts in this age of moons and missiles, of that inexorable thing we call progress, there's bound to be some sentimental foot-dragging, a certain yearning to assert some vestigial claim on whatever is poetical or even sublime in what is past, and to capture and to imprison it in the unfeeling present.

Something of this nostalgic impulse is implicit in this old schooner's purpose, her predestined enshrinement at the voyage's end. For all her prosaic pedigree, her last sailing is symbolic of all the grand and lofty ships that passed this way before her.

Fifty years ago, these Northwest waters were crowded with the Cape Horn elite, some coming, some going, others loading or waiting patiently on demurrage for their turn to stand under Tacoma's great grain elevators and tip the dusty gold horn of plenty into their freight-hungry bellies.

One by one they glided up these narrow wind-swept waters, from Bath and Searsport, from Rockland, Camden and Yarmouth—Maine's lordly *A. J. Fuller*, named for the Downeast country doctor who crossed Sagadahoc ferry to deliver my mother of her Woolwich son; Carleton & Norwood's *Wandering Jew*, with her big, cambered, flush deck designed to shed the Cape Horn combers; Minott's *James Drummond*, as white as the hilltop church of her

12

native Phippsburg, the three-skysail yarder, *Henry B. Hyde*, mightiest of all the Downeasters. And their big iron and steel English rivals, like *Balclutha*, whose glory the *C. A. Thayer* is destined to share in San Francisco's perpetual harbor of living sail relics.

> Lochs, Counties, Shire, Drums, the countless lines
> Whose house-flags all were once familiar signs
> At high main-trucks on Mersey's windy ways
> When sunlight made the wind-white water blaze.

Up the Sound and through the Strait of Juan de Fuca to a safe sure offing outside Cape Flattery.

This is the way they did it in Masefield's WANDERER days. This is the way also of our unpretentious going in the *C. A. Thayer*.

The schooner's cook thrusts his white hat out the galley door and waves the supper bell. The entry in the schooner's log reads: "5:10—Steering after the tug, keeping the tug on the starboard bow."

On deck, the gear is on the pins. The chaos and confusion of getting ready has been cleared away.

In the forward house, the watches are wolfing white platters of roast beef and vegetables to the cook's delight—and dismay. We have stores in the lazarette for a fortnight, but what is this!

Dr. Roderick Norton of Tacoma, the ship's surgeon who doubles in crockery and aluminum pots, shovels out two wrappers of bread and big ironstone pitchers of cool milk. There's a keen edge to the evening air, so eat up! And let's hope for a big lift in the winds that blow down out of Alaska.

"7:28—Point-No-Point abeam."

The men lay aft and muster in the waist for the sea-rimed rite of choosing up the port and starboard watches.

Sea manners say it's the mate's turn first. "Kortum," he growls. A big fellow in a red jacket moves out. Last passages are an old song to Karl Kortum. He was an able seaman in the last passage of the old Bath bark *Kaiulani*, Gray's Harbor to Durban by way of Cape Horn, and Durban to Hobart where the old Sewall square-rigger was cut down to a barge and the gang paid off.

Now it's Johnnie Gruelund, the second mate's turn: "I'll take Harry Dring." The big Dane who began his career as a merchant mate in the old schoolship, *Danmark*, knows the unflinching stuff that Dring is made of, for Dring, too, is an old *Kaiulani* hand. They work together now in the high rigging of the *Balclutha*, keeping her taut and trim. Harry, who is down on the articles as third mate, moves over beside Mr. Gruelund.

"Riehl," barks the mate, latching onto the schooner's third member of the *Kaiulani* alumni association. Gordon grins as he takes his place beside Kortum.

"Gordon Fountain," counters the second officer. A man who looks almost too young to have sailed with Admiral Byrd on his second Antarctic discoveries in the barkentine *Bear of Oakland*, shuffles over the line.

"Davies," calls the mate, and Big John, a civilian personnel officer at the Alameda Naval Air Station, joins the watch.

"Shannon," says the second mate, pointing to the swashbuckling secretary in the shipfitter's local of San Francisco.

This ends the rite of the waist, three men to a watch in the time-honored choosing that is like draft day in the National Football League.

These are the men of the first team, the hard core for the hard work that waits outside the heads. All but Shannon and Davies have been in sail.

Bosun Harold Huycke of Tacoma gets the rest, the carpenter, Gordon Jones; and Frederick Fischer, a Seattle shipbuilder, the carpenter's mate; and Capt. Philip Luther, a Washington State pilot commissioner; and Axel Widerstrom of San Francisco, son of a shipmaster who sailed deepwater in Bath ships of the House of E. & A. Sewall. Axel, a telephone company employee, is down on the articles as radioman.

Axel Widerstrom's work as a telephone technician ashore grew out of the interest he developed in the unfolding age of ocean wireless that was still a new thing when he was a boy.

While Axel was still going to grammar school, his father used to take him on summer voyages to Alaska aboard the *Star of France* and the *Star of Holland*.

The summer Axel sailed north with his father in the *Star of Holland*, the Alaska Packers had installed their first wireless equipment in this fine old ship which was formerly Brocklebank's *Zemindar* of Liverpool. It was during that *Star of Holland* summer that Axel was bitten with the wireless bug that sparked his interest in electrical communications enough so that he chose it as his life work.

As late as 1928, Axel's father still was taking a big full-rigger to the north. And this year, he left one there—the *Star of Falkland*. Off Akun Head, on a misty morning, the mate tacked ship without permission. At the moment the *Falkland* struck, Captain Widerstrom was attending a seaman dying of pneumonia in the 'tween-decks. The seaman's death followed closely that day the death of a ship.

The official inquiry exonerated Captain Widerstrom.

On board the *C. A. Thayer*, Electrician Axel Widerstrom—keeper of the electric generator, the lamps and borrowed voice radio—rounds out the company of specialists.

These are the bosun's day men who will ply their skills and brawn to the jobs he will set them to. The schooner's hard-driving young bosun is a licensed shipmaster, too, making three on board. Yes, the *Thayer's* is a hand-picked crowd.

Both Second Mate Gruelund and Bosun Huycke are schoolship graduates. Johnnie Gruelund was schooled in the Danish full-rigged sail-trainer, *Danmark*. His father, Capt. Peter A. Gruelund of Randers, Denmark, is an old-country authority on the last days of sail.

Bosun Huycke was schooled at Occidental College, the University of Southern California and the California Maritime Academy. He has served as mate in ocean steamers. As a steamship company executive ashore, he has pursued a maritime hobby that goes back to his teens as a boat keeper for Santa Monica fishing excursions.

Today, his maritime collection of logs and ship lore is one of the most impressive on the West Coast. His writings in this field of maritime history marked him for the special assignment by the State of California's Division of Parks and Beaches to oversee the fitting out of the *C. A. Thayer* as a permanent maritime relic.

It's the mate's watch. "Turn to, the port watch!" The rest drift forward. But they are in no hurry to turn in. They gather in the lee of the forward house. This is no ordinary voyage. This is the last, and the men linger in the darkness.

Six bells ring out aft. The big bell on the foc's'le head answers, and a voice cries out in the night, "Lights are bright, sir."

Karl Kortum . . . The man who originated the *C. A. Thayer* project and tied it together is a Cape Horn sailor.

This is the way of sailing ships almost since the beginning of time. But this schooner's going is different. For hers is a sentimental voyage, perhaps the last Pacific passage of sail.

As a floating museum, this stout wooden survivor of West Coast sail will depict in enduring documentary form the hard old marlinespike kind of seafaring that sparked the pioneering way of the West's maritime growth and progress.

As nearly as all this adds up to any one man's doing, the credit points aft to the dark shadow at the helm where the binnacle light falls on the strong, gentle face of Director Karl Kortum of the San Francisco Maritime Museum. In a way, this sentimental journey bespeaks his cheerful defiance of Masefield's mournful song:

> They mark our passage as a race of men
> Earth will not see such ships as those again.

It began nearly ten years ago—this dream of Kortum's—in freedom's classic fashion, with a letter-to-the-editor, datelined Petaluma, California.

A shipmate with whom he had sailed in the little four-hatch freighter, *San Antonio*, had sent Karl a clipping from *The Christian Science Monitor*, describing a project taking shape at Mystic, Connecticut, to restore two historic ships in appropriate oldtime surroundings.

The story stirred Kortum deeply. He had just returned to the family farm at Petaluma after a voyage around the world that began in the lovely Downeast bark *Kaiulani*. He had rounded Cape Horn and the Cape of Good Hope. In the five-year interlude, a World War had intervened. Kortum had left as an able seaman in the *Kaiulani*. He returned to the Golden Gate as Chief Mate of a steamer.

Kaiulani was the last square rigger to take her departure for Cape Horn from San Francisco. Throughout the 1930's Karl had watched their numbers dwindle in the ship graveyards around the bay. Harry Dring, Jack Eatherton, at times other sea-minded fellows, would make pilgrimages with him to these disconsolate old Downeasters and West Coast barkentines and Clydeside craft. Their fascination lay in the imagery of what they once were.

For Karl Kortum, that imagery and the start of the whole thing began with the N. C. Wyeth illustrations in "Westward Ho!" His Uncle Leslie had given him a copy of the book as a boy. His cousin had a copy of "Sail Ho!" filled with pen sketches by Gordon Grant aboard the *Star of Alaska*. That weaned him from Wyeth galleons to later day windjammers. There were still *Star* ships—tall and tangible—tied up in Oakland Estuary.

In the 1930's, there were sporadic proposals to preserve one of these square riggers. Karl, still a boy in Petaluma, read accounts about these attempts in the San Francisco papers. He hoped fervently to see one of them succeed. A committee was formed to save the *Star of Finland*, but nothing jelled. A few years later, with rising freight rates brought on by the war in Europe and the shortage of ships, she put to sea again under sail. Harry Dring and Kortum were aboard.

That was in 1941. It was now six years later, but the clipping about Mystic kindled the old fires. Kortum wrote a letter to the Mayor of San Francisco urging that his city save the *Star of Alaska*, then languishing near Los Angeles. Jim Walpole, who had been in *Kaiulani* (the renamed *Star of Finland*) with Harry and Karl, pushed Mrs. Spreckels' doorbell one night. They had a you-get-us-in-I'll-do-the-talking split. But nothing resulted from either of these efforts. City Hall talked about money, and Mrs. Spreckels talked about ship models.

About this time, the State of California projected plans for a freeway through the Kortum family farm. In the course of resisting this, father and son went down to San Francisco and ended up by paying a call on Scott Newhall. He was then editor of the "This World" section of the *Chronicle*.

Seeking newspaper support in their fight, on a rainy November afternoon they stood in Mission Street pondering where to turn for help, and ended up by paying a call on Scott. They had always subscribed to the *Examiner*, but did not happen to know anybody there; nor anyone at the *Chronicle*, either. But Hall Newhall had been another in the *Kaiulani* crew and he had told Karl that he had a brother who was an editor there and who had once sailed a ketch to Mexico. So the two Kortums went to that newspaper office. Earl Warren rode up in the elevator with them. By the time that particular night was over he was not Vice President of the United States and Harry Truman was President for a second term. Scott received the Kortums courteously and saw to it that they got a potent story about the opposition to the freeway.

Some months later, Karl Kortum read a review Scott Newhall had written about the latest sailing ship book by Alan Villiers.

It led Karl to think Newhall might be the man to respond to restoring the *Star of Alaska* and putting her among a selection of
sympathetic craft at Aquatic Park. In 1940, Karl had attended a
jam session in the Casino there and that marvelous empty pile
appeared to be a likely prospect for a maritime museum. He
wrote a long letter to Scott, and Frank Eatherton painted a water-
color scene of the *Star of Alaska* tied up at the Municipal Pier
with the museum in the foreground.

This time it clicked. Scott Newhall not only liked the idea;
he worked out a technique by which it could be launched. And
he set up the personnel to launch it. San Francisco is in his debt
for the changes wrought, and that will be wrought, at Aquatic
Park.

Karl Kortum was to come down off the farm. He had proffered
the plan as a worthwhile civic project, with Harold Huycke or
John Lyman to head it. But Scott insisted that he be hoist by
his own petard. Kortum didn't resist very hard—he was fascinated.
Scott persuaded Paul Smith to spring Dave Nelson from his writing duties on "This World," and Dave and Karl were sent out to
explore the climate for the project. When they reported back
that it looked good, Scott Newhall reckoned that the best chance
of success was to throw the plan open to all four daily newspapers
for support—a civic project for the benefit of San Francisco.
Accordingly, a meeting of the four publishers was arranged at
the Bohemian Club, and a little presentation booklet describing
the plan was prepared for each of them.

Kortum was thrilled by all this, of course. He embellished the
plan with a steam schooner and the three-masted lumber schooner,
C. A. Thayer, as fitting companions for the square rigger. The
perfect panoply of West Coast shipping!

Kortum had been aboard the *C. A. Thayer* in 1941. Harry
Dring and he had made it a point to hitchhike up to Seattle and
look at her schooners while *Kaiulani* was taking aboard the lumber
cargo down at Grays Harbor. The *Thayer* was in every way
typical of her period, and at that time was still rigged with dead-
eyes. She was shabby, but things had since picked up for her
and in 1949, on the eve of the publishers' meeting, she was the

last of the California-built schooners still keeping the sea. That fact spoke for her soundness, and that's why Kortum felt that she should represent her type.

On land, Kortum suggested a dramatic new use for Aquatic Park—an old-time San Francisco plaza flanked with period buildings; the Hyde Street cable car line led into it; a Victorian station at the end of the line; the Haslett warehouse converted into a railroad museum, and the like. Hugh Buell, *Chronicle* staff artist, made drawings and paintings of all this. Great to dream!

The four publishers listened to the fantasy, and said, "Yes." The Bohemian Club, after all, is where a portrait of Robert Louis Stevenson looks luminously down from the wall. They studied sketches of the *C. A. Thayer* and the full-rigged ship and scow schooners and steam schooners and the diamond-stack locomotives that Gil Kneiss had clung to precariously all these years and they said, in effect: Do it. Put it together.

It was an act of faith that could be called peculiar to this city, because they talked less of how than of a test of the San Francisco spirit. The dreamers were given their charter under the old City-That-Knows-How formula—and little else in the way of instruction.

The first thing was to assemble the Maritime Museum proper—a headquarters. The Mayor was pleased to provide that magnificent empty casino on the shores of the lagoon. Kortum rounded up a Villon's army of unpaid sea lovers to scour the city for models and relics, and to work at night readying them for display. Mrs. Spreckels gave her collection, which was the nucleus. She and the shipping companies along California Street gave funds for paint and lumber and glass. All winter Max Lembke, who spent his boyhood on the decks of the four-master, *Helene*, led a little band at Sausalito engaged in chiselling off the bow carvings of the schooner *Commerce*. Scott Newhall welded a great stand of channel iron to support it. Ken Glasgow of the *Kaiulani* crew helped Karl in pulling it all together. They opened May 27, 1951.

Two years ensued. The instrument that is played by ear was in need of both resin and a wild Highland air. Jean Edmonds, soon to be Kortum's wife, had come to work as a volunteer secretary. Every year now they were hosts to a quarter-million museum visitors. But Karl was still living on savings and Jean on the tag end of the steamship company donations. Ed Harms, president of the board and prober for funds, moved to New York. Glasgow had to go back to sea. The Kortums waited each week until enough coins accumulated in the donation box in the lobby to frame and hang a new sailing ship picture.

The impetus, the spark, the talisman needed was the old Clyde-built sailing ship, *Balclutha*, the *Star of Alaska* of Gordon Grant's book, the vessel Kortum had come down to San Francisco to save. She would take the museum beyond mere ship models, out-of-doors, on to capture the whole of the park! She would be real and San Francisco would take her to its heart and would encourage getting a lumber schooner and a steam schooner and the diamond-stacked locomotives to keep her company.

Kortum decided to give her back her original name when he found an old T. H. Wilton photograph of her showing that when she was *Balclutha*, she was port-painted, that most elegant way to decorate a ship. The year in the shipyards in charge of her restoration was the pleasantest year of Kortum's life. But the year that preceded it, when he struggled with the philistines in his own organization so that they might buy the rusty and half-dismantled old ship, and with the owner to forge out a price, and not money enough—"that was a sheer hell of anxiety;" said Kortum in retrospect. The *Balclutha* was the pivot on which the whole future turned.

The owner towed the ship up from Los Angeles and beached her on the Sausalito mudflats. The museum started a fund drive —they called the project Argonaut Bay now. Sydney Walton was president, Bob Mayer, vice president. They worked prodigiously. Indeed, Mayer all but held the corporate structure together in these uphill times. John Cushing of Matson had faith and got his company to donate $10,000. Bill Mills headed up the Ship Committee. This was 1953.

Tom Ingersoll, Joe Moore and John Riley of the shipyards offered initial repairs if the museum took title, and that helped. And Harry Lundeberg went to the Governor to get *Balclutha* a berth. When an option was finally granted by the owner, Hugh Gallagher got twenty prominent San Franciscans to underwrite a note for $20,000. When the "Argonauts" drydocked her and found the ship sound and bought her, Mario Grossetti came forward with help from the shipyard unions, swarms of skilled men. And T. C. Conwell drummed up tens of thousands dollars' worth of supplies and services.

Done! It was plainly time to be getting on to something else. One day Kortum had been to see Jack Dickerhoff at Moore's in Oakland about some rigging problem. Driving through the square at the foot of Broadway, he saw Mr. Joseph R. Knowland—his gray locks whipping in the wind—dedicating a bronze bust of Jack London. Karl stopped and took a picture and went on, troubled at this incarnation of opportunity. Mr. Knowland's family had operated sailing schooners up and down the coast of California and Oregon; he was known as a champion of western history; and he was chairman of the State Park Commission, which had millions of dollars in tidelands oil royalties to allocate.

A bill in Congress had given these funds back to the states; at least a portion of it would go for historical monuments in California. President Truman vetoed it; President Eisenhower signed it. Kortum, eyeing this bonanza, had first suggested restoring Admiral Farragut's *Hartford* with tidelands oil money. Marc Cremer suggested Dewey's old Union Iron Works cruiser, the *Olympia*. For a time, too, in the early days, they made a try for the *Kaiulani*, the bark that started it all, but she was in Manila, dismantled, and too costly. The museum's focus turned back to getting the *Star of Alaska*.

The museum had a president at this time who matched the publishers' concept of the San Francisco spirit. Kortum proposed in a letter to Hugh Gallagher that they marshal all their friends— the publishers to give their respectability at City Hall and Harry Lundeberg to win the Governor's ear—that the time had come to seek a schooner, the *Wampa*, and turn the Hyde Street Pier into a state historical monument.

There is an old West Coast chantey:

> For there's plenty of gold,
> So I've been told,
> On the banks of the Sacramento!

Kortum and Dave Nelson drove up to the state capitol to committee hearings. Gallagher had got Tom Maloney to introduce a bill in the Assembly. He had persuaded Mrs. Spreckels to contribute funds to hire the skillful Dave as an advocate, full time on the project. The Kortum's first baby, little Jeanie, busied herself upsetting office waste-baskets while her mother worked late into the evenings to get out oceans of correspondence. The bill moved along. Publisher Charles Mayer saw to it that the *Examiner* gave Page One support.

Right here, a good word must be said, too, for Tom Ingersoll of the Maritime Museum's Board of Directors. When, not unnaturally, a storm developed within the board over trying this time to save wooden ships, the General Manager of San Francisco's big Bethlehem shipbuilding plant flew up to Seattle to inspect the vessels. Stopping at a drug store to buy an ice pick and a flashlight, Ingersoll probed the ancient rigs and planks and satisfied himself that the vessels were worth saving.

Meanwhile new difficulties arose in a well-mounted drive by civic groups who wanted this money to be spent for a new park at the historic old San Francisco Ferry Building.

The Ferry Building Park forces had their own religion and more troops. But in San Francisco at that time there was muscle that originated in the four-masted bark *Muscoota* and in the bark *Oaklands* and the barkentine *Forest Pride*. Kortum would go down and see Harry Lundeberg and he would give a growl at the right time—because the boss of the Sailor's Union had a soft spot in his heart for the old ships.

The project emerged from that 1955 session of the Legislature without a single dissenting vote. But the Governor finally had to put over approval of all the claims staked out in this new Gold Rush until calmer times next spring. Mr. Knowland and his fellow members of the State Park Commission, Mr. Newton P. Drury, Chief of the Division of Beaches & Parks, and Dr. Neasham, the State Historian, invited the museum people back, asked questions and recommended to the Governor that saving the old ships be made into law.

That is how the *C. A. Thayer* came to be pulled off the gravel at McDaniel Cove.

Meanwhile, Kortum suggested to Drury that Captain Raynaud,

who had surveyed the schooner *Wawona* once for Ken Glasgow and Karl (they had thoughts of putting her to sea) would make a good team with Harold Huycke. They handled things in the

Beached and forlorn . . . In a cove on the Olympic Peninsula, Kortum found her masquerading as a "Pirate Ship."

north and did a fine job of seeing the schooner through the shipyards at Seattle and Winslow.

Down in California, the State had put Ronnie Miller in charge of her fiscal voyagings.

Later, the state instructed Captain Raynaud to buy the *Tongass* (to be renamed the *Wapama*), the steam schooner that pairs off with the *Thayer*. Newton Drury, warmly supported by DeWitt Nelson, Director of Natural Resources, had thrown behind the old-ships project all the political skill that in other days he used to save leagues of California redwoods. He has become a conservationist of shipping.

The Museum forces engaged in one more skirmish—or short war, if you will. It was necessary if they were to finish the fantasy filed at the Bohemian Club those many years ago. They called it Project X now. Their opponents, meaning the new Mayor and most of Downtown San Francisco, rallied grimly behind the Ferry Building Park. The sum of $2 million was at stake. To better ornament their claims, the Museum's fleet of old ships— now counted among the municipal jewels—was to be captured and towed off to moorings at the foot of Market Street.

The Museum had a courageous president in young R. Stanley Dollar, Jr. He stood up to City Hall as the storm swept across the front pages. But by now the Museum forces were skilled at firing from first one embrasure and then from another to give the effect of many soldiers in the citadel. The Ferry Park skirmishers were beaten off.

The State Park Commission handed down its decision and ended the struggle. The $2 million could not be spent at the Ferry Building because of a new hideous freeway in front of that edifice. Kortum's plan got the money instead. Project X—the old Argonaut Bay fantasy—became the dignified San Francisco Maritime State Historical Monument.

The following day, Karl Kortum left for Seattle to join the C. A. Thayer—for a sailing ship voyage, the carefree life in the foc's'le, for him certainly one of life's great pleasures.

After the Old Man scans the stars, he peers ahead through the mizzen shrouds toward the towboat's mast lights as though sniffing out tomorrow's wind. He ducks down the cabin ladder, bends over his chart table and, in the light of the swinging lantern, makes the night's last entry in the log:

"11:05—Dungeness Light abeam."

The towboat is working out into the dark strait and, on the after end of the long dipping hawser that is making phosphorus snakes in the water, there's a hint of a lift to an old ship's bows.

Chapter III

"A Fair Wind, Captain!"

Monday's dawn came in dripping with fog, narrowing down the horizon around the *C. A. Thayer.*

The schooner's logbook still was only a laconic check-off list of beacons that passed in the night.

"12:45—Race Rocks abeam.

"02:25—Sheringham Point Light abeam.

"03:35—Ship Point abeam.

"05:57—Tatoosh Island Light abeam."

An enormous gray agate coffee pot was bubbling on the red-rimmed galley range, and Clark Turner, the cook, was up to his elbows in breakfast batter.

Out ahead of the schooner, the rhythmic drive of the *Trojan's* diesel horses carried aft between the dismal wail of Tatoosh Island's fog signal.

Forward, the men tumbled out one by one and slumped, sleepy-eyed, around their steaming white mugs and mounds of hot cakes.

In the swinging gray world outside the little square window, the big airhorn on Cape Flattery was carrying on the morning's eerie colloquy with the fog whistle on the *Swiftsure* Lightship fourteen miles across the greasy entrance to the fog-bound strait.

The wind was southwest, one knot. The *Trojan* kept drumming westward, dragging the schooner out beyond the 30-fathom curve. The log said:

"07:28—*Swiftsure* Light Vessel abeam."

The tug stood on to the westward for nearly another hour before Captain Raynaud said quietly to Mate Dickerhoff, "Mister, I guess you can cast those gaskets off your fores'l."

Time to let go . . . The schooner signals the tug to stop towing.

There was a rush of heavy boots along the main deck as the mate came to the forward end of the poop.

"Do you want power on the gypsy leads?" inquired Dring, the keeper of the donkey engine.

"What, with this crowd?" scoffed the mate. "Sweat 'em up by hand. Stand by your jib halyards!"

One by one, the towering headsails were two-blocked on the run.

"Get that fores'l on her." This one did not go up so easily. There was no running these halyards down the deck. The mates cried out the tempo as the men swayed in unison. "Vast heaving on the throat halyard! Heave away on the peak. Keep that gaff level."

The mast hoops inched up the heavy coating of linseed oil on the new masts, sticking at every pull. Out of the side of his mouth, the mate reminisced, "How would you like to be in *Camano* with only four men forward?"

"Understand this," said the mate, "just one man will give the orders here!"

Seeing the halyard start to lose ground back through the block, Dickerhoff spurred the men on sardonically, "When you get tired of losing it, you'll hang on to it."

It was brutal going, a few inches at a pull. A shrewd judge of pace, the mate relented for a moment. "When you get your air, pull again . . ."

"08:27—Let go tug. SW by W ½ W."

Up went the stubborn old mains'l. The jib-headed spanker was easier.

"09:40—Set course to south southwest magnetic."

The *Trojan* hauled in its hawser and circled back toward the schooner. A voice bawled out of the pilot house, "Fair wind to you, Captain."

Captain Raynaud waved back, "Much obliged."

"Wait 'till the bill comes for this fourteen hours' towing," grinned the mate. "Or are we California taxpayers paying for this one?" he added, remembering that the *C. A. Thayer* belongs now to the California Division of Parks and Beaches.

Letting go the towline . . . With a windjammer mate's suspicion of tugboatmen's motives, Mr. Dickerhoff spurned the modern bridle and kept the hawser's end aboard ready to slip.

Captain Raynaud's sailing plan is something only time will reveal to the gang forward. Shipmasters, if you please, are not given to sharing their professional secrets with hired hands—not even dollar-a-trip men like the eager crowd taking the *C. A. Thayer* to sea for the last time.

Even so, all the sail-worshippers berthed forward are bursting to know. They are keyed up for this chance to close out the schooner's sixty-two sea-wandering years with a grand finale—

The tug turns back . . . The *Trojan* leaves the schooner outside the Straits of Juan de Fuca.

a West Coast sailing record, maybe, that will make surviving shellbacks remember how—

Angels with silver trumpets blew
The song of glory that was you . . .

There is more "brass" aboard than you'll find around a binnacle, meaning licensed merchant masters, and Naval Reservists who had wartime sea commands. They count themselves lucky to be dirtying themselves in the tar pot on this uncommon voyage.

All this tension, this talk of speed, takes me back to newspaper days when I was covering the Grand Banks racing schooners in the ding-dong deep-sea battles for the Halifax *Herald's* Cup some thirty years ago.

Tall, sail-crowded ghosts from Gloucester and Lunenberg dance again on my mind's horizon. Gloucester's crack schooner, the *Gertrude L. Thebaud*, and her big, ungainly Nova Scotia rival, the champion *Bluenose* from Lunenberg, and the great company of Grand Bankers that came before them—the *Haligonian*, the *Elsie*, the *Esperanto*, the *Henry Ford*, the lovely white *Elizabeth Howard*, and the incomparable *Columbia*, next to the *Mayflower*, perhaps, the fastest schooner either Storey or James of Essex ever built.

I remembered when these Downeast schooner queens and their captains went to battle for the sailing supremacy of the North Atlantic fisheries, when skippers clamored for the chance to sign on as ordinary sailors—much as, in Seattle, Capt. Adrian Raynaud was besieged before the *C. A. Thayer's* departure.

Like the Downeast fishermen of a generation ago, the schooner *C. A. Thayer* has codfish lines in her genealogy, too. In the summer of 1950, Seattle citizens scanned the story in their Sunday supplements that foretold the schooner's arrival with a record haul of 190,000 codfishes!

"Homeward bound from Bristol Bay, the last remaining schooner sailing from Puget Sound to Alaskan waters is due back in Poulsbo, Kitsap County. The schooner is Capt. J. E. Shields' *C. A. Thayer*, skippered this year by the Captain's son, Ed."

"There's always a doubt each year about whether the *Thayer* will make another voyage," said Captain Shields' younger son, John. "But there's never any doubt about a market for the fish she catches."

The reason there was a market for the 190,000 codfishes the *C. A. Thayer* brought to Puget Sound as late as 1950, was that the *Thayer* had no important competition. Only a wooden ship can be used to catch codfish in Bristol Bay and bring them to the Sound. And only a windjammer, a ship without a fuel bill, could make the trip with profit. "Besides, you can't put codfish into an iron ship," John Shields explains. "The salt would destroy the ship and the rust from the iron would destroy the fish."

Indeed, the *Thayer* had no competition at all after the 1947 Alaska codfishing season, when her big Bendixsen sister *Wawona* (named for a high site in Yosemite Park) went north for the last time. The *C. A. Thayer* was the last of the Bristol Bay saltbankers.

A pierhead gam . . . Capt. "Codfish" Kelly and Capt. J. E. Shields mull over old times in the Bering Sea. Cáptain Kelly sailed the *Wm. H. Smith* out of San Francisco; Captain Shields took the *Thayer* north from Seattle.

But burly Capt. J. E. Shields was never a man to let barnacles grow on the keel of a good thing. He knew it the moment he laid eyes on the *C. A. Thayer* in the mid-1920's. He got a few Bering Sea voyages out of her before the depression hit. After that, she lay idle for a decade.

Commandeered by the U. S. Army in World War II, the dismantled schooner became an ammunition barge in Prince Rupert, British Columbia.

Shields, the shrewd Bluenose, still knew a good thing after the war when he re-masted the *Thayer* with three spars salvaged from the old *Sophie Christenson*, a famous contemporary Captain Shields himself sailed in the Bering Sea codfish trade.

For a few seasons, the *C. A. Thayer* was back in business for what was to be her final sea quest—in the role of a subarctic cod-chaser. Her 1950 voyage to the Bering Sea was her last.

The tug had melted into the fog astern. Slowly the schooner fell away on the starboard tack. A faint murmur of wake began to bubble under the transom. Inshore, the air horn on the *Swift-sure* gradually grew fainter.

All at once, the *C. A. Thayer* was back in another world and another century, unattended by land or time. She stood stiffly in a narrow circle of sea birds and aimless swells.

Where was the wind that was lurking in our dreams of a record passage? Everyone began to wonder. Even the ship didn't seem to like this state of affairs with the sails hanging almost helpless in the light going. The gear groaned disconsolately, and aloft the gaffs slatted and banged at the schooner's every roll and scend.

When the *C. A. Thayer* was launched in 1895, she joined what was soon to be one of the finest schooner fleets sailing out of San Francisco. The 1896 Lloyd's *Register* lists her as the sole vessel in the E. K. Wood Company's name, but, by the turn of the century, an infusion of capital set the northern shipyards humming. The *Fred J. Wood* joined the earlier Hall-built schooner, *E. K. Wood*. Various combinations of Hitchings and Matthews and Joyce—Humboldt Bay shipbuilders now moved to the timber stands around Grays Harbor—launched the *Defiance* and *Daunt-less*, the *Fearless*, *Resolute* and *Alert*. These doughty names were all four-masters.

The company lumber yards in San Francisco were at the head of Channel Creek, above the Third and Fourth Street bridges, and beyond where the hay schooners catered to the city's horse population. This vaguely named estuary, sometimes called Mission Creek, sometimes Third Street Channel, was all bustle then. Its upper reaches, above the present banana docks, are somnolent today.

Even then, San Francisco was a "cosmopolitan" city. Scandinavia was certain to be well represented in the port, forward and aft, when the new schooner took the water in the '90s. C. W. Liljeqvist was the *Thayer's* first master. He left the little one-topmast schooner *Charles Hanson* to join her and he was in command for five hard years in and out of the lumber ports. A photograph shows him when he later became master of the larger *Fearless* for the company. He stands on the deck load with a spade beard and derby hat, looking as valiant as his schooner's

Off Cape Flattery . . . Alone in a gray world, the *C. A. Thayer* starts her voyage home.

name. Ole Monsen followed Captain Liljeqvist aboard in 1900; then came Gus Peterson, followed by Erik Ingman.

G. J. Peterson, who may have been the same Gus come back aboard, had her in the first part of 1910, and by October, Fred Scott, her former mate, took command. Mrs. M. A. Dore of Hoquiam on Grays Harbor recalls visits by the E. K. Wood captains to her home when she was a girl. Her father, Carl Baker, was foreman for the company ashore. Captain Peterson, she recalls, took his wife and their little daughter, Carolyn, to sea with him in the *Thayer*.

Fred Scott must have been cut out of very stout sail cloth, too. L. E. McKinlay of Aberdeen knew Scott as a young man sailing coastwise in lumber schooners soon after he jumped an English ship in San Francisco. Scott later became Port Captain on Puget Sound for the Weyerhaeuser lumber steamers.

McKinlay was a passenger in the *Thayer* on a lumber voyage from Hoquiam to San Francisco in June, 1906. From the *C. A. Thayer's* anchorage off the Barbary Coast, San Francisco was a

Her first captain . . . For her first five years, C. W. Liljeqvist was the *C. A. Thayer's* master. This old photograph of the officers and crew of the schooner *Fearless* shows the captain with beard and derby hat standing at the left of the group on the deckload.

picture of desolation. A few modern buildings were still standing here and there but most of them were gutted by the fire that raged after the earthquake.

San Francisco's ill wind was anything but that to such lumber companies as E. K. Wood, whose schooners were pouring in lumber at a prodigious rate for the re-birth of the city.

Right here, it may be useful to assess the practical attributes of the *Thayer's* "bald-head" rig which was typical of some 120 West Coast schooners.

The term stemmed from the steamboat type of mast which was made with a long-tapered pole extending above the spring stay band. The masts were considerably taller than the masts installed in vessels with topmasts. The large masts were 130 feet long, and measured 30 inches in diameter in the deck. Usually the masthead measured 12 feet and 15 feet was the length of the pole. The masts carried a larger spread of canvas than the sails on topmast schooners of comparable length.

A woman from her past . . . Capt. Fred Scott's widow recalls a mighty gale in a conversation with historian Harold Huycke in the *Thayer's* cabin.

Gordon F. Matthews, a native of Eureka, knew the origins of these bald-head schooners as intimately as any West Coast sailing authority. As a shipbuilder at Hoquiam, Washington, he took a keen interest in the records and history of sailing vessels operating on the Pacific Coast.

The first West Coast bald-header was the four-mast schooner, *Novelty*. This 592-ton schooner was built in 1886 for the Simpson Lumber Co. of San Francisco in their shipyard at North Bend, Oregon. She was timbered with Douglas fir.

Outward bound for Honolulu . . . Deckloaded at Hoquiam, Washington, with only inches of freeboard remaining. Capt. Fred Scott poses at the taffrail with Mrs. Scott and a girl friend whom she invited to make the trip.

Gordon Matthews' unpublished records show that H. D. Bendixsen built the first three-mast bald-head schooner at his Fairhaven shipyard in 1887. She was the 290-ton schooner *Esther Buhne*. He also built the 230-ton three-master, *Czarina*, in 1891, smallest bald-header built on Humboldt Bay. His *C. A. Thayer* was a medium three-mast bald-header. Two years later, Bendixsen launched the 468-ton *Wawona*, largest of the bald-head three-masters built on the Pacific Coast.

Bendixsen built about twenty of that type of vessel from the same model. He increased length, breadth and depth to increase the lumber capacity sought by different owners.

The Simpson yard at North Bend built the first five-mast, bald-head schooner, the *Louis*, gross 831 tons, in 1888. She was the first ocean-going five-masted schooner ever built, and the smallest in tonnage of that type built on the Pacific Coast. She was owned by Simpson. The late Capt. Ralph E. Peasley of Aberdeen, Washington was her master for several years.

Several owners converted vessels to the bald-head type for economy in operating. This paid dividends.

The last vessel built before World War I, was the three-mast bald-head schooner *Oregon*, gross 343 tons, in 1905 at Prosper, Oregon, by John Heuckendorff.

Bald-head schooners became very popular in the lumber industry. They proved to be very economical and efficient to operate, especially in the coastwise trade. They did practically as well as the topmast schooners and were a tribute to their builders and the courageous men that sailed them in strong competition.

Prior to 1906, a large number of the three- and four-masted and five-masted bald-head schooners were built on the Pacific Coast. Here are the master builders who built one or more of that type of vessel:

Simpson Lumber Company	North Bend, Oregon
H. D. Bendixsen	Fairhaven, California
Bendixsen Shipbuilding Co.	Fairhaven, California
Peter Matthews	Eureka, California
George H. Hitchings	Hoquiam, Washington
Lindstrom Shipbuilding Co.	Aberdeen, Washington
John Heuckendorff	Prosper, Oregon
Frank Stone	San Francisco, Calif.
John Dickie	Alameda, Calif.
Pacific Shipbuilding Co.	Marshfield, Oregon
Thomas McDonald	Hoquiam, Washington
T. C. Reed	Ballard, Washington
Charles Fulton	Bellingham, Washington
H. R. Reed	Port Madison, Washington
Mr. Hughes	Port Madison, Washington

These well-known shipbuilders in their time were credited with designing and building the vessels that had the largest lumber capacity for their net tonnage anywhere in the world. They would sail empty with only enough ballast for trim, and carry over 50 percent of the lumber cargo on deck when fully loaded.

The largest schooners carried a yard with square-sail on the foremast which gave them a larger sail area to spread more canvas in favorable weather.

The bald-head schooners were a favorite berth with the sailors, particularly in the coastwise trade. In the beat to windward on the return trip north, there was no climbing aloft to shift the top-sails when tacking. Consequently, there was more of the abundant life on those vessels.

A very important improvement in the evolution of these schooners was the construction of a fore deckhouse large enough to accommodate a forecastle and galley. The foremast was installed down through the house to the step on the keelson. The deckhouse provided more light and ventilation for the forecastle, which made a more comfortable place for men to live, improving their health and morale.

Another valuable improvement in the late '80's was the donkey hoisting engine. The deckhouse was built longer to accommodate the steam engine with boiler and feed-water tank. With a swinging cargo gaff rigged and installed on the main mast, the hoisting engine was used for loading and discharging cargo.

Auxiliary gear was installed on top of the deck for hoisting sails, mooring the vessel and weighing the anchor. That important improvement replaced the laborious old hand-gear method.

The topmast schooners had advantages in sailing in light winds on trips to Australia, for instance. But many of the bald-head schooners made fast passages on off-shore trips. The three-mast schooner, *Azalea*, gross 394, built in 1890 by Bendixsen, loaded redwood clears in Eureka for Sydney. With a return cargo of coal loaded in Newcastle, she sailed home to Eureka in 52 days. This was considered to be a very fast time for a vessel of her size when loaded with coal.

The four-mast bald-head schooner, *Salvator*, gross 467 tons, built in 1890 in Eureka by Peter Matthews, loaded redwood lumber for Sydney and made the voyage in 52 days.

One captain, in telling how fast his vessel could sail, remarked, "The harder I sail her, the higher the bow goes."

Some shipowners preferred topmast schooners; others operated both types of schooners, coastwise and off-shore.

For several years before World War I, shipping was in a depression. The schooner fleet on the Pacific Coast had declined and values had depreciated sharply. In fact, freight rates were so low most of the fleet was tied up. Some survived the depression; some were scrapped.

The effects of the war in Europe reached the Pacific by 1915, and the demand for Pacific Coast lumber to be shipped to ports around the Pacific rim increased freights and charters for depressed schooners. In 1918 and 1919, freight rates were the highest ever paid for shipping lumber and coal cargoes in foreign trade.

The bald-head schooners were in on the demand the war had created. The value of vessels increased year after year. Some vessels were sold for more than their original cost. Ship owners "never had it so good."

Shortly after the Armistice in 1918, demand for charters began to decline and rates were reduced. After 1920, world shipping conditions declined to the extent that a depression in shipping was world-wide.

A number of schooners were lost during the war years and some were sold for other purposes. The four-mast bald-head schooner *Dauntless*, gross 548 tons, built at Hoquiam in 1898 by George H. Hitchings, was sold to a buyer in Los Angeles. The vessel was reconditioned and converted for marine moving-pictures.

The following bald-head schooners joined the Puget Sound codfish fleet:

> *Azalea,* gross 344 tons, built at Fairhaven in 1890
> *Charles R. Wilson,* gross 345 tons, built at Fairhaven in 1892
> *C. A. Thayer,* gross 453 tons, built at Fairhaven, 1895
> *Maweema,* gross 453 tons, built at Fairhaven in 1895
> *John A,* gross 282 tons, built at Eureka in 1893

The schooners loaded their supplies and sailed for the Bering Sea in the late spring. There they caught the codfish, and when the captain decided he had enough fish salted down and stowed in the hold, the vessels returned to Puget Sound in the late summer. The fish were discharged at the several plants and processed there for the markets.

The bald-heads were very practical vessels for the codfishing industry and some very fast passages were made on the return trips with the prevailing winds to drive them across the Gulf of Alaska to Cape Flattery and on to their home ports on Puget Sound. One captain, who was master of the *John A.* for several years, claimed she could outsail anyone although she was the smallest vessel in that fleet.

During the years they operated in that industry, the fleet landed thousands of tons of the Bering Sea codfish that were processed and shipped to markets in most of the States.

Right after Pearl Harbor, vessels of all types were in demand for war service. Consequently, the codfish schooners eventually were taken over for that service. Some had their spars and rigging dismantled for towing as cargo barges.

After the end of the war in 1945, some of the vessels were fitted out and operated again in the codfish industry. However, the increased cost of keeping up the old schooners finally forced owners to lay up their vessels.

Several of the bald-head schooners never returned to Puget Sound after the war. Some years ago the *Charles R. Wilson* was sold to a firm in British Columbia and was moored as a breakwater to protect log booms during stormy weather.

Most of these schooners were built out of Humboldt pine, the same timber as Douglas fir, tough and durable.

The majority of the shipowners operating vessels in the lumber industry on the Pacific Coast were located in San Francisco, the home port for their vessels. A number of the owners had a preference for the vessels built with lumber cut on Humboldt Bay. No doubt that was the principal reason for the large number of the bald-head schooners having been built there.

After Bendixsen established a permanent shipyard at Fairhaven, he erected a sawmill to cut long logs into the long timbers required for building larger vessels. The long timbers cut for keels, keelsons, and other timbers, also for the ceiling, plank and deck timbers were essential for the construction of larger and stronger vessels.

The Humboldt pine never grew to quite the size of some of the Douglas fir of Washington, for use in production of clear lumber, for door stock, and finishing lumber. However, for structural purposes, it contained the qualities for strength and long life.

Climate also was favorable for longer life for the vessels built on Humboldt Bay. The rainfall was about 35 inches a year. The prevailing winds from spring to fall were from the Northwest— dry winds that, doubtless, dried the timbers, reduced the moisture content, and gradually and thoroughly seasoned the lumber before the vessel was completed and launched. The *Thayer* is a good example of a vessel built under those favorable conditions.

Air circulation in wood construction lengthens the life of the lumber and helps to prevent dry rot. Vessels are exposed to considerable dampness and it is essential to provide for free ventilation through the hull.

Although salt is not considered to be a preservative for lumber unless it is continually replaced, the codfish schooners did carry considerable salt that apparently helped to preserve their timbers during their time in the codfish industry.

There were a number of four-mast bald-head schooners built in shipyards on the Pacific Coast. They were a very practical-rigged vessel and an important vessel for the lumber trade, both coastwise and off-shore.

Many of them made very fast passages sailing under favorable conditions. The smallest of that type of vessel was the *Defender*, gross 446 tons, built in 1896 by H. D. Bendixsen. The largest of the type was the schooner *Forest Home*, gross 763 tons, built in 1900 by J. Heuckendorff at Marshfield, now Coos Bay, Oregon.

The financing for the contracts for building the vessels involved considerable amounts of money in those years. There were shipping companies, also lumber companies which could contract with a shipbuilder to construct a certain type of vessel, it being customary to specify the lumber capacity of the ship. They would offer shares of the vessel to investors who were interested in investing their capital where they could expect good returns on their investments.

For instance, assuming that a vessel could be built for $20,000, the managing owner might decide to take one-quarter for himself.

He then would offer the remainder to subscribers, who would take 1/10th or 1/16th share each. Sometimes others divided the vessel shares into 32nds, thirty-two 32nds being the whole. A number of companies retained control of the vessel and a few wealthy companies owned a vessel outright.

The fore gaff jaws carried away . . . Carpenter Gordon Jones and his mate, Fred Fischer, had it aloft again by the afternoon watch.

Some shipbuilders were obliged to take an interest in order to get a contract to build a vessel.

H. D. Bendixsen was the owner in more vessels he built than any other builder.

Many of the captains owned an interest in the vessel in which they were master. It was customary for a captain to sell his interest to another captain in the event of change of masters. Another custom was that the shipowner would ask the ship chandlery firm to buy an interest. That firm built up the trade by taking an interest in as many vessels as it possibly could manage. Other firms did likewise.

The grocery firm, the butcher, the sail-maker, the firm that made the rigging owned shares in vessels.

When the contract for building the vessel was completed, the managing owner would issue a Bill of Sale to each shareholder for his interest. These were filed for record in the U. S. Customhouse. The complete records of ownership of all vessels are filed there for the protection of each owner's interest. It is impossible to take that away or transfer that interest before the owner signs another Bill of Sale when he agrees to sell his interest in the vessel.

The managing owner collects a stipulated commission of the vessel's gross income for the services as manager.

Customhouse brokers are familiar with the vessel's records on file in the Customhouse and they write up the Bill of Sale for ownership or transfer of ownership in all vessels documented and registered in the many U. S. Customhouses. The brokers are reliable and their fees are reasonable for the services rendered.

New masts. New standing rigging. New cordage. But how much of this will these tired, old sails take without wearing themselves to rags? Roll and bang.

The mate's frown kept eyeing things aloft. Then:

"10:40—Starboard side of fore gaff jaws carried away . . ."

Jones and Fischer, the carpenters, turned to.

". . . Lowered fores'l and repaired same."

At noon, the taffrail log showed twenty-four miles made good from *Swiftsure* Lightship.

"12:45—Set fores'l."

Roll and bang. Roll and bang.

"12 Midnight—Steering southwest magnetic. Vessel laboring gently in cross swell."

Roll and bang. Roll and bang.

Chapter IV

On the Main Hatch

Mr. Gruelund's entry in the schooner's log was plain and right
to the point: ". . . day came in calm and clear . . . 0430 . . . wore
ship to starboard tack. Wind North East one knot." Probably it
is just as well that logs are not kept by men with purple pencils.
But it was a beautiful morning.

The second mate's cheerful Nordic face popped out of the
after cabin. He paused at the top of the companionway with his
sextant cocked, scanning the fading stars and the listless sea
around us.

"Oh ho," he exclaimed. "Visitors!"

A crowd of forlorn little land birds had congregated along the
gunwales of the captain's gig. A meadowlark was solemnly surveying his rumpled plumage in the first streak of day. The nearest
land was Cape Avila, fifty miles to the eastward.

There were goldfinches, juncos and russet towhees, resting up
after their long landless journey, orphans of some distant storm,
perhaps. One of the finches was making a commotion trying to
keep her balance on the spinning white line of the taffrail log.

Mr. Gruelund braced himself at the rail and went about his
business with the stars.

Mr. Dickerhoff eyed his junior skeptically. "If you ask me,"
he growled to the helmsman, "fancy navigatin' ain't for these old
tar pots."

Perhaps the chief mate is right in feeling that the schooner's
navigators are overly ritualistic, what with not only the traditional
Noon sun sight for latitude, but morning and evening star fixes
as well. All this zeal may stem from the fact that the second
mate and the bosun were cradled in schoolships.

"Fancy navigatin' ain't for these old tar pots" . . . Said the mate, as he turned to study his art of sheets and halyards.

Such tautness, too, makes startling contrasts with what life must have been like aboard the *C. A. Thayer* in her Alaska salmon salting days—an interim outwardly less taut and trim than that of her timber droughing period.

Capt. "Whitehead Pete" Nelson had been a shrewd business man, but he was never her captain. That title was a courtesy conferred on a managing owner who wasn't afraid to bear a helping hand anywhere around his ships or salteries.

It isn't hard to imagine the contrast between the present poop load of "celestial" wizards and the scene that Whitehead Pete's widow recalls aboard the *Thayer* some 46 years ago, when the schooner went sloshing up to Alaska with a clumsy wooden scow slung outboard of the mainmast and, of all things, a cow munching hay down the main hatch.

"Pete made a padded stable for her," Hilda Nelson remembers, "just big enough for the cow to go in."

Thrifty Pete Nelson had three vessels at different times in the northern trade, nibbling around the corporate fringes of such cannery giants as Alaska Packers and Libby, McNeill & Libby.

U. S. Bureau of Fisheries records show that Peter Nelson s salmon saltery was an important industry unit in the early part of the century, although the salt salmon trade as a whole "was so overshadowed by its giant brother, the canned salmon trade, that it is frequently lost sight of or swallowed up in the latter."

Underway for Bristol Bay . . . "Whitehead Pete" Nelson bought the *Thayer* in 1912 to supply his salmon salteries in Alaska. The schooner gets a good slant and a rousing sendoff outside the Golden Gate.

As early as 1902, Nelson had a salmon saltery about 10 or 12 miles above the place in the Igushik River where it enters Nushagak Bay.

The drift gill net was the favorite gear in this bay. Occasionally traps were used. The fish run was known to begin very early in Nushagak Bay. Kings usually appeared about June 5; reds about June 5 to 8; cohos either late in June or early in July; dog salmon around the middle of June; and humpbacks about the same time.

Fishery bureau reports for 1913 noted that "this year Peter M. Nelson, whose former salting station on the Igushik River was absorbed by the Alaska Fishermen's Packing Company in 1910, built and operated successfully a small plant of similar character near Koggiung. Some of the material for this plant was brought from the old Bear Creek saltery near Port Moller."

And in 1918, bureau reports noted that "all the losses that year in the western district of Alaska were sustained by Peter M. Nelson at the Kvichak saltery, and consisted of 3,300 barrels of pickled salmon, valued at $75,000, and damages to the wharf of $2,500."

Squaw Creek: "Whitehead" Pete's salmon boats . . . This photograph made in 1923 by Harry Nelson, the *C. A. Thayer's* chief mate, shows the type of boat used in Alaska. John Englund, the owner's nephew, standing in the foreground, was winterman at the saltery. The *Thayer* can be made out moored in the distance.

There were six sailing vessels tending the western Alaska salteries that year; 189 sail-and-row boats were used; 26 launches under 5 tons, and 23 power vessels over 5 tons. Alaska produced 56,890 barrels of pickled salmon in 1918 as against 36,390 the year before. The value of the Alaska salmon pack that year was $1,079,881.

It was a bad year for ice in the subarctic fisheries. While the *C. A. Thayer* weathered it successfully, the Bureau of Fisheries steamer *Roosevelt* (Peary's old Maine-built polar ship) extended aid to a number of cannery ships distressed in the ice. The

Roosevelt rescued 21 men from the *Tacoma* who had been encamped on the ice for some days after the ship sank.

The *Thayer* left San Francisco April 28, 1912, on her first salt salmon quest, carrying, beside the Nelsons' cow and the ungainly scow, a big deckload of lumber for a second salting station. The schooner also carried enough salt to pickle two cargoes of salmon and shooks enough from Carl Cooperage Company of San Francisco to hold them.

After nearly 50 years, Whitehead Pete's widow recalls vividly that the "veather vos ver-r-ry bad. Ve had a dicken of a time to make it. In the *Thayer*, ve had to go this vay, and that vay, and that vay, and that vay—and sometimes ve couldn't go at all. . . . They call it 'Heave to'. . ."

When she visited the *Thayer* after nearly half a century, Hilda Nelson surveyed the schooner's after cabin and reflected: "There vos a sofa and a rocking chair and a kind of byu-rrow and there vos everything there—nice furniture. And they got loose, and they came roaring in. And I cried. And little Rudolph says, 'Ma-ma, don't you cry! I'll dance the klip-klop for you'. . . ."

A native son of Sweden's shoe-string shaped Oland Island, Whitehead Pete Nelson landed in San Francisco in 1890. Working his way up in the salmon business, he became beach boss for the Alaska Packers at Nushagak. "If you're so good for the Packers," Hilda told him, "if they like you so much to make you beach boss, you are good enough to work for Pete Nelson."

At the time, Nushagak was crowded by the Alaska Packers Association canneries and a colony of Moravian Missionaries, selflessly bent on civilizing Eskimos from May to September. Pete cocked an eye toward Igushik. At the same time, the Nelsons sounded their savings and brought up $7,000 to buy the old Matthews-built four-mast schooner *Salvator*. They spent another $10,000 fitting her out. The first season, though, they chartered the *Salvator* for $300 a month. When business flourished, White-head Pete opened a second station at Koggiung—on the other side of the bay from the Alaska Packers' big canneries and the Moravian Mission at Nushagak. Later, Pete set up a third and final station at Squaw Creek.

Most of these cannery and salt salmon stations lay near the head reaches of Bristol Bay. The Fisheries steamer *Albatross* found that "the winds and weather in Bristol Bay and the other parts of Bering Sea visited . . . from the last of May to the first of September may be summarized in a few words. . . . It was boisterous weather nearly all the time, but seldom rough enough to interfere with our work."

In 1890, the *Albatross* reported: We had several summer gales of moderate force, but no severe storms. Fog and mist prevailed, and a clear day was the rare exception."

Beside the *Salvator*, chartered for the first Alaska venture, Whitehead Pete commissioned Billy Cryer in Oakland to build five launches, the *Hilda*, the *Aletha*, the *Olga* and a couple of others whose names do not come so readily to Hilda Nelson a half century later.

But it is the 1912 salmon season the Whitehead Pete's widow remembers above all the rest. Nelson's saltery fell into the hands of a cookhouse faker, a Norwegian who had a flair for ingratiating himself with unwary Alaska proprietors, and for inciting mutinies by palming himself off as a cook.

Hilda Nelson recited the bill of particulars from memory: "That Norvegian, he gave them all sour moush and sour bread and sour everything—except eggs. He couldn't sour them up. So he done away with all the eggs. Ve had to go to the Alaska Packers to get eggs."

All this fanned resentment in the Nelson camp that burned like a slow fuse leading up to a barrel of salt codfish. That the fuse was tied to a barrel of fish instead of gunpowder seems all very natural as Mrs. Peter Nelson tells it after all these years.

"My husband used to catch some codfishes; and then he salted them and barreled them—lov-ely codfish; and then he comes back to the station with it, and opens the barrel. Then here comes the cook, that Norvegian, Johansen, and lays a board right across the open barrel and puts his vash basin right there, and vashes himself good.

"Then my husband comes and says that I don't know that ve ate codfish in soap suds. He says, 'I never know that. That's the first time I ever saw.' Then the cook, he took off he apron, and rolled it up, and slings it in my husband's face, and. . . . 'I kvit!' he says.

"Vell, my husband, he comes to me, and he says, 'Now, vaht do ve do?' So I says, If you 'll give me a little help like he had, I vill cook. Ve had two great big stoves side by side. They didn't get no more sour moush."

One woman cooking for 47 hungry men! "Fishermen, fishermen, fishermen, that's all I saw that summer," Mrs. Nelson recalls. "I didn't bother about the fellows. I say, Hello, Nels, or Hello, Carl; Hello, Larz; Hello, Oscar . . . and that ended it. If anybody said to me, 'That's good bread you've got. Now it isn't sour,' I said, "I'm glad you liked it."

Whitehead Pete's spunky better half wasn't the only woman on the beach at Nushagak the summer of 1912. The Nelson saltery had chartered the old Bath bark *W. B. Flint* to help carry the season's pack to market, and Captain Smale's wife went north for the season. But somewhere protocol got its wires crossed. The wife of the proprietor of Nelson's salteries found herself playing second fiddle to a woman whose husband was in Pete Nelson's employ. When asked were there any other women up in Bristol Bay that year, no wonder Mrs. Nelson quickly replied: "None at all, except when we had that bark, the *W. B. Flint* . . . there were Mrs. Smale . . . She vos . . . she vos . . . she vos high-toned."

The crew of the *C. A. Thayer* are, almost to a man, collectors of sailing ship lore. They have signed on to sail the schooner to her new destiny as a State maritime historical monument for the satisfaction in what is the schooner's last voyage, wanting no wages out of this sentimental journey, save in the meaning Masefield sang—

> To give her beauty, though
> ourselves have none,
> And let the others have the
> wealth that's won.

"This is something beyond my wildest dreams," admits Dr. Roderick A. Norton, husking corn for the crew's supper. The Tacoma pediatrician has been purse seining up to Ketchikan for fun and has crewed in racing yachts on Commencement Bay; but never in anything like this ancient lumber schooner, where it takes a gale to drive her and muscle to work her.

"Penny and Jim didn't see how I could get along on this voyage without them," said the strapping six-footer who comes a-flying out of the galley at every call for all hands to bring the schooner over on the other tack.

Penny Jane Norton had a hand in packing her father off to sea. "Tell them about Captain Norton's Sea Chest," urged Clark Turner, the schooner's cook. The doctor everybody calls "Bill," felt around the spices on the galley shelf and took down a gilded minature trunk no bigger than his fist. Bill brought Penny's box out on the main hatch for the watch to see. Inside the lid, his 11-year-old daughter had written: "Starboard is right; port is left."

Dr. Norton plucked out a little packet of pink paper on which were the words: "Just a pinch." Inside was some paprika. Next came a tiny porcelain dog—the "mascot," and a candle no bigger than a match, "so you can read in bed."

Penny should have heard her dad chuckle at this, exclaiming, "That's a laugh. When do I get any chance to read in bed?" Hadn't the irrepressible Harry Dring routed him out of his bunk that very morning at the first peep of dawn with a shake and a cheerful, "Come on, Doc, you're wanted in obstetrics!"

And after shining his lantern in the doctor's face, he had left the startled sleeper to cogitate on the rattling of the stove lids overhead where the cook already had the morning oatmeal on to boil. In some ways, the reorientation in nocturnal habits from a physician to a sailor must not have been hard to make.

Bill Norton's sensitive surgeon's fingers felt inside the little gilded chest and drew forth an apron no bigger than his thumbnail. "For the galley," thought Penny. Next came a can opener, labeled, "Open sesame." And at the very bottom, a little plastic whistle—with a tag that said, ". . . . . .If you need me!"

Sailors and idlers clustered around the ship's doctor on the main hatch like little boys at a birthday party, watching the presents being unwrapped.

An erect, strong-limbed six-footer, something in the hearty way he tails onto the sheets and halyards at the mates' commands suggests he may have developed that brawn as a football player in his undergraduate days at the University of Michigan. But he very quickly dispels this notion by baring his white, even chompers. "You don't see any missing, do you?" grins the doctor. As a sailor, anybody can see Bill Norton is a natural. Even his trip up the inside passage to Ketchikan—something that was "like a row of postcards all the way"—isn't in it with crewing in the *Thayer*, an assignment that confirms him in his unobtrusive role as a seagoing workhorse.

On the other side of the main hatch, Gordon Riehl chuckled and resumed the letter writing that goes with his hobby of dropping notes in bottles into the sea and patiently waiting for the years to bring one of them back.

September 18, 1957
At Sea
Aboard the three-mast
schooner, *C. A. Thayer*
bound to San Francisco
from Seattle

"To the finder of this note:

"Please forward this note to the following person, giving your name and address and where you found this bottled note. It would be greatly appreciated and of interest to the children.

"Our position at noon today was Lat. 47° 02′ North—Long. 126° 10′ West.

"I am enclosing a photograph of this schooner having new masts stepped in Winslow, Wash., U. S. A., in July 1957. Thank you. 'Jim' Gordon Riehl, 2716 South East 75 Ave., Portland, 6, Ore., U. S. A."

Once on the long passage of the steel bark *Kaiulani* from Durban to Hobart, one of Riehl's bottled notes had washed up on a beach and, long after Gordon was home from the last voyage of the *Kaiulani*, the postman in Portland delivered a letter from an excited boy in the south island of New Zealand, saying he had found the *Kaiulani's* bottle.

Gordon Riehl's authentic sailor background—from a 14-foot catboat on the Columbia up to a Cape Horn passage in the steel bark *Kaiulani*—had its firming up in years of prowling the old sailing ship hulks from Astoria to Portland. His penchant for tracing old ship pedigrees took him to sea as a steamship deckhand the year he was 18. First in the *Alice Tebb* out of Grays Harbor to San Pedro. Then in the *West Ira*; and soon in another old Hog Islander, the *West Cactus*, freighting beans and rice to Puerto Rico.

Just as he was about to ship in the *West Cusseta* for a China voyage, young Riehl heard that the *Star of Finland*—none other than the Sewalls' beautiful Bath-built *Kaiulani*—was fitting out for sea once more.

This was early in the 1940s. Sinkings were way up, and so were ocean freight rates, luring old windjammers into newness of life, the incomparable life of tall canvas and cordage that had sung its romance into Jim Riehl's adventuresome soul.

Either Capt. Hjalmar Wigsten of the *Star of Finland*, now re-named *Kaiulani*, was a very sentimental man or a very hard-pressed one, because Riehl got word to hurry up and join. With enemy submarines on the prowl all out over the world's trade routes and sailing ships being notorious sitting ducks, plainly there was method in Wigsten's wire. He needed a crew and they weren't to be found in Union hiring halls.

Jim joined at Aberdeen, shook hands with Kortum and Dring, Jim Walpole, Jack Henricksen, Bill Bartz, and said to himself, "If these greenhorns can take it, I guess I can." He signed on as ordinary seaman.

Hall Newhall, another starry-eyed sail worshiper and a brother of the San Francisco *Chronicle's* Executive Editor, Scott Newhall, was also in this devil-may-care cast readying the *Kaiulani* to load lumber at Aberdeen for Durban by way of Cape Horn. Scott Newhall was later to become a back-stage power in the affairs of San Francisco's new Maritime Museum.

These and young Paul Soules, strong of shoulder, captain of the University of Washington's winning crew at Poughkeepsie, and his brother, Tom, were the nucleus of the *Kaiulani's* last crew, the crowd who sailed her around the Horn and on around the Cape of Good Hope to Hobart, Tasmania, where the bark was cut down to a barge, her tall wings clipped for good.

Although this fine ship has long since passed out of the registry, many of her last crew still muster occasionally—Riehl, Kortum and Dring of the *C. A. Thayer* and Kenny Glasgow, Bill Bartz, Hall Newhall and the Soules—to sing the old songs and relive the high memories of this memorable last voyage in square-rigged sail.

The *C. A. Thayer's* arrival at San Francisco was fated to precede by not many weeks the word of Capt. Hjalmar Wigsten's death —Wigsten of the *Kaiulani*. For some time the Old Man must have sensed that his number was flying on the hoist. For in a letter to an old shipmate, the last Wigsten ever wrote, the *Kaiulani's* last captain wrote: "I'm like an old ship, blocks and gear falling down from aloft. . . . ."

At the next reunion of the *Kaiulani* men there will be much that is new and some things that are over for old shipmates to talk about—the last voyage of the *C. A. Thayer*, the old Cape Horn adventure to rekindle, too; and, finally, a toast: "To Wigsten!"

Gordon Riehl's bottled note from the *C. A. Thayer* splashed into a flat sea.

". . . 1820—Wore ship steering SSW. Barometer 30.10. Weather calm and clear."

Chapter V

Light and Baffling

The *C. A. Thayer* was bound south from Seattle to San Francisco but the schooner's long, rakish bowsprit was pointing back toward Seattle. There is nothing more frustrating, nothing so forlorn, as a windjammer without a wind.

The rudder's rusty pintles thumped in their iron gudgeons and, aloft, the schooner's heavy gaffs slammed and banged in aimless arcs across the cloudless blue infinity.

Gone was the dream of a record passage. Nearly a week had slipped by since the schooner took her departure from the *Swiftsure* Lightship. After another day's almost due southerly drifting, the *Thayer* still was not quite on the latitude of Gray's Harbor. The next day's run was a little better. Three long tacks had carried the schooner past the Columbia River's offshore current and a little below Tillamook. But the great rock was bearing east by north some 50 miles inshore.

Forward, the men began to grumble, as sailing ship men will when the wind holds light and baffling. They gazed disconsolately at the chart of Puget Sound tacked on the messroom bulkhead. Well, at least we're off that chart. But why didn't somebody forward bring along a coast chart? "I gave the Old Man mine," said Phil Luther a little apologetically. Perhaps the Washington State Pilot Commissioner feels some proprietary negligence in forgetting to fetch two. "I sure would like to know how Washington made out in their football opener Saturday. Why didn't one of you guys think to bring along a radio?" Clearly Luther didn't relish stopping all the barbs.

"Why doesn't the Old Man stay in close, instead of getting hung up out here 50 miles off the beach?" persists Luther.

"And why shouldn't he stand off?" another fo'c's'le kibitzer wants to know. After all, a schooner doesn't steer steamboat courses. Or does she?

"It's the set of the sails" . . . And not the gales that tells them the way to go. Capt. Adrian Raynaud and his two mates.

There is purpose in Captain Raynaud's skittishness about hugging the beach. First, perhaps, a deepwater sailing man's inherent dread of getting caught on a lee shore, becalmed and set in on fog-shrouded ledges by tricky ocean currents. Here on the North Pacific coast they never set twice in the same direction or velocity on any two voyages. Government sailing directions stress this plainly.

Then, too, Captain Raynaud is counting on the autumn equinox, when the winds haul around into the northwest and drive out of Alaska with steady force. Also, he harbors the sailing ship man's reluctance about venturing into the steamer lanes with the ever-lurking risk of collision at night.

With her running lights showing only 10 feet above the water, a schooner is hard to see. Nor do sailing vessels show a white light, which is the light that carries farthest. And how many steamer captains these days ever caution their mates at night to keep a sharp lookout for sailing vessels? Nobody who has not held command knows much about responsibilities that weigh down the distinction. How many men aboard have ever worked a heavy lumber schooner along the coast? Who is there here to say how Capt. Ole Lee, for instance, would have sailed her? Captain Lee had the *Thayer* on her second Australian voyage; and in his schooner coasting days, he always hugged the coast sailing south to San Francisco. To that extent, pilot Phil Luther's views square with coastwise schooner custom. But now we are only second-guessing Captain Richard Quick's former mate.

Beside, there's nothing much in all this dreary speculation that a good breeze won't dispel. When it does pipe up, doubtless we'll all sing a different tune.

And now what do you call this that's flinging long catspaws across the glassy blue swell? What is it, if it isn't some wind!

Mr. Gruelund ducked into the cabin singing softly to himself.

". . . . 6—Wind freshening from southeast. Vessel making about 3 knots for the first time in 3 days . . . . 12 Noon—Distance by observation 28 miles."

But Aeolus, the wind god, is only having some fun with us. There's another darkness of aimless sloshing. And at daylight, more of the same.

"Wednesday, Sept. 25 . . . . 12 to 4—Vessel hardly making way through water. Hauled in the taffrail log. . . ."

It was no surprise to the morning watch finding the mains'l lowered in a great brown heap on the main hatch and deck. The

Close-hauled and not much wind . . . "And she still gets along at 3 or 3½," said the mate. "I'd call that the mark of a smart little ship."

other watch already was plying palm and needle to the job. So were the captain and mates and Bosun Huycke.

Chief Mate Dickerhoff surveyed Gordon Fountain sitting on the boom stitching a small patch at the head of the sail's throat. "Take big stitches," admonished the mate. "That's the best way to make em hold in old canvas."

Captain Raynaud honed his sheath knife in a professional way on a steel bar, cut a square of canvas from the new bolt and turned the edges under with the back of his knife. With quick even stabs, his sail needle went around the edge of the patch, putting even the chief mate to shame.

59

Patching the mains'l . . . Captain Raynaud and chief mate Dickerhoff were expert with palm and needle.

There's an air of cheerful competence about this unruffled captain whose apprenticeship at Haviside's later passed Richard Quick's eagle eye when young Raynaud turned to on Bath's big *Edward Sewall's* three suits of Cape Horn sails.

Thursday, the fourth day at sea; perhaps Tillamook marks the turning point in the weather, for the old schooner is beginning to get up and go. The noon latitude sight shows 111 miles on the log by observation. The *C. A. Thayer* still is far outside the land. But the lazy compass card has a story to tell, hovering cheerfully on south southeast. At least we are headed toward San Francisco.

Yaquina Head on the Oregon coast lies abeam at supper time, some 30 miles inshore. And Heceta Head's ten-second flash still is too far off to sight in the night.

Mr. Dickerhoff was in one of those expansive moods that seems to come up like a breeze and sweep men's words before them.

It made him almost lyrical remembering the *Lottie Bennett*.

"We discharged the deckload in Suva but we still had 450,000 feet of finished lumber—tongue-and-groove and the like—stowed below for the Australian sugar mill at Lautoka.

"So old Captain Twentyman and his Kanakas took us out through the reef and we were on our own. It blew up strong in the Kandavu Passage and we lost a mains'l; blown right out of the bolt ropes. I got all hands up and we bent another one without wasting any time. Lautoka is on the leeward side of the island.

"We worked the *Lottie Bennett* in toward the entrance, but the wind fell light and then we found that the current was setting us in toward the reef. Captain Harris tried to get her onto the other tack—it was getting desperate—but the schooner wouldn't come about. We were getting closer to the reef all the time. The crew had their suitcases packed and out on deck by now. It looked like the end of the *Lottie Bennett*.

"Captain Harris went down below. I took charge on deck and tried the same thing I tried here in the *Thayer* the other day. Hauled the fores'l over, got sternway on the vessel, and backed her around on the rudder. It worked and I went down to get

Captain Harris. The captain and his wife were praying. Well, their prayers were answered."

Mr. Dickerhoff paused to scan the compass swinging lazily across southeast by east.

"It was hard times—back in the depression—when I joined the *Bennett*; there wasn't much doing along the Estuary. I was working one day a week at General, leader man, but that wasn't hardly enough to live on. One day I crossed over to the Oakland side to see if there was a job going in the tugs. Now, there were several vessels laid up in the General yard, mostly steam schooners, but also the *Lottie Bennett*. Glancing back from the Oakland side, I saw some men looking around on her. I beat it back to Alameda and, knowing the watchman, he let me into the yard. I went down to the schooner and hit up the Harris brothers—that's who they were—for a job. They had been pilots out on the Yangtse and had operated the old barkentine *Mary Winkelman* until she went ashore on the reef outside Pago Pago in 1923.

"Well, getting back to Alameda, when the Harrises had asked me some questions about what vessels I had been in, they offered me the job of second mate. I had asked for A.B.—and glad to get that. Next day, the schooner was hauled; we walked around underneath her. The bottom was fine; I told them that if I were them I would just caulk the butts. They offered me the job of Chief Mate—$105 a month. I tell you, it looked as big as a house to me."

At that stage of the tide in the affairs of an old schooner, the *Lottie Bennett* couldn't have been much to look at. Mr. Dickerhoff shook his head almost sadly surveying the scene in retrospect.

"She had been laid up several years without a shipkeeper—ever since that Frenchman from Tahiti, Ozanne, had given her up for the old *Annie Johnson*, which was old but had an iron hull. The *Lottie* had been the *Normandie*; the *Annie* became the *Bretagne*. Old Ozanne had his whole family aboard, including a good-looking daughter, and Kanakas for crew.

The Chief Mate's recollection of the hard plight of the poor old *Lottie Bennett* left nothing to the listener's imagination.

"The paint was scaling and flaking—worse than here—and the

Painting.

doors were swinging wild on the hinges. The window glass was broken in the deckhouses. The shipyard went about setting all that right; on deck they caulked the waterways and around the hatches. My concern, same as back in Seattle with the *Thayer* this time, was to get the *Lottie Bennett* ready for sea.

"Harris, the one who was to go captain, left it up to me once he got my number. I hired seven men, all good riggers I knew, and we went at the ratlines first so you could get aloft. Harris used to come over about 11 o'clock. If some one hit him up for a berth, he'd send them over to me. He gave me $250 to buy what we needed right away. I kept the money in the leaves of my daybook."

Jack Dickerhoff was 27 years old at the time. "Of course, there weren't sails enough. I told Harris about the Sanders & Kirchmann schooners you could see on the end of Government Island. The *Samar* and the *Philippine* were there—the *Samar* was a fine big schooner, laid up since Asmussen brought her back in the early twenties for the last time. That was ten years before, but Kirchmann wouldn't sell either of them for some reason. There was plenty of good gear aboard them.

"Harris went to see Kirchmann and got him to let us have the pick of the sails and gear for $2,500. I hired a tug and lighter and went alongside, much to the surprise of old Captain Fredrickson in the *Philippine*, shipkeeping for the two of them. I gave him the letter from his owner. He put on his gold-rimmed glasses and read it. It must have been a blow; he figured that one or the other of the schooners would get back to sea again. And the old captain must have figured that meant he would, too. I had my men with me; Captain Fredrickson had no choice but to unlock the lazarette and the bosun lockers forward. But he protested at the old canvas we left behind. He still had hopes, the Old Man did.

"When we got back, we dragged the sails up on the wharf and laid them out. The *Samar* was a much bigger schooner than the *Lottie Bennett*; I took two cloths off the leech and re-roped the sails."

The chief mate's burly shadow paced leisurely back and forth in the overtaking starlight. "It was too bad we came back empty, but our time charter for copra fell through. For a while, it looked

Scraping.

like we were going to take empty oil drums to Java, through Torres Strait. We got busy repairing the sails. The sailmaker at Suva was old McGovern. Both Harrises were aboard and they both had their wives, and one of them was pregnant. She didn't think much of roaming around too long all over the Pacific, so we came home instead of going to Java."

". . . . Friday, Sept. 20 . . . . 12 to 4—Fair and clear, steering SE magnetic. Vessel rolling gently in quarterly swell. 8 to 12—Wind falling off. Crew employed in scraping forward part of poop."

"Crew variously employed" . . . A busy ship is a happy ship.

The log shows 373 miles from the *Swiftsure* Lightship, with Coos Bay bearing just forward of the beam some 20 miles to the sea buoy. If only the wind holds up, another day's run will see us well around Cape Blanco. Perhaps that word "Cape" has an ominous sound for Captain Raynaud—

". . . . 12:30 Noon—Jibed ship to starboard tack. Steering south southwest magnetic. 7:45—Vessel rolling heavy in beam swell. Gear and sails standing up fairly well. Overcast with light drizzle. Barometer 29.95. . . ."

—Meaning, with night closing in, Captain Raynaud has turned away from the Cape, standing offshore for the night.

The next 24-hour run was something to cheer about. The hurrying wind puts a rousing new lilt into Gordon Jones' accordion at the singsong in the dog watch. A few more days like this and we'll be home telling about how the *C. A. Thayer* reeled off 185 miles from noon to noon. The schooner came about on the latitude of the Oregon state line, well south of Cape Blanco. At last we were around the corner!

While there's a grain of truth in Shannon's remark that "we're halfway out to Hawaii, too," still the captain's purpose in standing west of the 128th Meridian becomes plainer. For if the wind holds, the schooner can clear Cape Mendocino and fetch the Farallones on one long tack.

But "ifs" are the stuff sail passages are made of. And they count up to a worrisome pile under the *Thayer's* harlequin array of borrowed sails. Something more effective and at times more fun is the schooner's borrowed radio telephone. It's an old windjammer's only concession to mechanical progress, her one link with the land. The captain had not wanted the radio on board. But the Coast Guard inspectors at Seattle had taken one cursory look at the tired old schooner and decided that a radio telephone was the better part of discretion.

Each night Captain Raynaud wrestles dutifully with its half-drowned static—fending off Dave Nelson's regular nightly inquiries for the ship's "schedule."

"But can't you give us some idea about your Estimated Time of Arrival?" persists the Maritime Museum's beach-bound master of

Sparks and Chips . . . Fred Fischer wields his old-time adze; Axel Widerstrom carries the radio battery forward for recharging.

waterfront ceremonies. "Just say the word when you want us to send the tug down to the Lightship with the press photographers to welcome you."

Between radio static and the banging of the heavy gear above the cabin skylight, the skipper is hard beset to convince the irrepressibly friendly Nelson that schooners are no respecters of schedules. Time enough to send a tug out to the San Francisco lightship when the *C. A. Thayer* sights the San Francisco Lightship. Out here off Cape Blanco it is still 1895.

A candle flickers on the slanting cabin table. Dave Nelson's voice fades; Captain Raynaud spins the knobs to tune Dave in again. The skipper has somehow switched to the fishermen's radio frequency. Confound it, what's this! A woman's voice blares harshly: "Hi, honey. I'm up here in my hotel room . . . My eyes? Oh, they're OK . . . I can see all right in the daytime. Enough to find you, honey, anywhere. You know me, baby; I cover the waterfront." Now, what's that all about, wonders the baffled schooner captain. The flickering candle limns his perplexed face, glints on the *Minnie A. Caine's* nickle-plated sea clock, casts dancing shadows on the cabin bulkhead. The devil take these new-fangled things!

". . . . Midnight—Clear and calm. Vessel rolling at times heavy in swell. 12:30—Lowered mains'l and observed several small holes. 4—At daybreak crew employed in repairing mains'l. . . . ."

This was the eighth day at sea and by evening the watch was jubilant at handing over a schooner with a breeze. The patched mains'l was pulling again. The schooner stood up to the new wind as stiff as a church. Whenever a sailor's drag bucket hit the water, it snapped like a strike on a marline's jaws. Guesses as to the schooner's speed ranged from five knots to eight. The *Thayer's* wake pretended it was fourteen. The old ship had found the glory road, the sky clear, the wind hard and steady, the sun sinking in the west in a perfect amplitude. For the first time, some of the men really knew what it telt like in a big wooden schooner with all sails hardened down to a good rap full.

At last the wind came fair . . . The big fore-and-afters strain at their sheets and give the schooner a day or two of good southing.

Chapter VI

The Mate Spins A Yarn

Radio weather reports told a tantalizing story of fresh winds close in along the land, feeding the fires of frustration among the discontented theorists in affable Phil Luther's arresting school of thought. Radio accounts of brisk northwest winds inshore seemed to vindicate their hunch about steering "steamboat courses" straight down the beach to San Francisco. There was nothing like an absence of wind to fan this debate. The schooner had lost her wind again.

The crew looked aloft disconsolately. And Chief Mate John Dickerhoff inwardly winced every time the wildly swinging gaffs fetched up ringing taut on their downhauls. Nobody knows better than the Chief Rigger of Moore Drydock Company in Oakland that art—

> . . . of masts, sail-crowded,
> Fit to break,
> Yet stayed to strength and
> backstayed into rake.

He knows, too, that there's a limit to how much of this heavy slamming the gear can take without coming all adrift—when there is not wind enough and yet too much sea.

". . . Tuesday . . . . Vessel drifting, does barely steer . . ."

Captain Raynaud dragged out the sailmaker's bench and sewed on the canvas boot he was making for the little engine that drives the bilge pump in the waist. "The best job in the ship," the captain remarked of his sail-making chores. Captain Raynaud had another talent—one that helped the chief mate pass the long night watches—he's the best yarn spinner I was ever with.

71

This morning, Adrian Raynaud's reminiscences of Capt. Richard Quick's old Cape Horner, and the big steel bark's hard-worked

A look at the throat halyards . . . The second mate goes aloft to see that the gear is clear of chafing.

sewing machine, did not flow so easily. We were victualed for 14 days, and now, nearly 10 days out, the captain was thoughtful. The next 24 hours' showing was even more dismal.

". . . 8:15—Tacked ship to port. Wind southeast . . . 8:45—
tacked ship to starboard . . . . 12 Noon—Distance by observation
38 miles . . . . 9:30—Wind hauled east, tacked ship to port. Vessel
hardly answering helm. Barometer 29.90."

The art of wooden ships . . . A half-finished scroll for the break of the
poop.

The wheel fidgeted a little, unattended.

Ah, what was this! The glass was going down. At last, the
wind? A cheerful look came over the faces of the schooner's
afterguard.

The wind showed promise of holding up. The wheel was kicking in its beckets. The mate sent a man aft to steer, ordered the watch to manhandle the spanker over to the lee side and swung it out with the boom tackle. Next, he dropped the jibs, slacked away the throat and peak halyards on the fore so that it spilled the wind. Even in the light going, the spanker edged her around onto the other tack.

The chief mate of the *C. A. Thayer* is a schooner man from away back, as if you haven't noticed by this time! He was chief mate of San Francisco's final lumber four-master, the Hall Brothers' handsome *Lottie Bennett*. That was in 1932. Five years before, when he was only 21, Dickerhoff was second mate of the barkentine *Centennial*. This beautiful softwood ship was built as a three-mast full-rigger by Smith & Townsend in East Boston 20 years before the *C. A. Thayer*.

Old timers remember how she was posted as "overdue" in the early '90s on a voyage from New York to San Francisco. Three times on this winter passage of Cape Horn she was driven back by hard westerlies when right off the pitch of the Horn. Twice she put into the Falklands for repairs. The third time, the sea outside Port Stanley was so rough, the *Centennial* limped all the way back to Montevideo to refit. She had the man worried who tolls the big bell at Lloyds in London, until finally she showed up off the Farallones in 199 days. After being burned to the water's edge in 1903, the *Centennial* was rebuilt and re-rigged as a four-mast barkentine.

"Frank Weidemann gave me the second mate's job. He had just bought her from Alaska Packers and had a lumber charter from Coos Bay to Melbourne." Dickerhoff recalled that this was in the spring of 1927 when freight rates were up, and a lot of old ships got away for a final fling.

"Weidemann had Walter Marzan as mate; Marzan and he had been master of the old *Star of India* at different times—the two of them had been sailing in the cannery ships for years; it was partly for old time's sake that Marzan got the job. I'd made passages up the coast in the *Alert* with Dirty Dan McDonald. In 1925, I was in the *Camano* up to Vancouver and from there down to Suva with lumber. I'd learned most of my schooner handling from Agidius, the mate in *Camano*. You wouldn't want a better teacher. What you don't know about, ask, was his motto. But still I was young and Weidemann said he would try me out, at least as far as Coos Bay."

Weidemann had high hopes for his old *Centennial*. Times had been dull after World War I, but this was the boom that was going to bring them back.

"He was a fine man, Frank Weidemann, no airs, knew his business; stood 6 foot in his socks. I can see him now down the skylight, hands behind his back, marching up and down the long saloon to some old German march he used to play on his gramaphone. He was happy to be in sail again. But this was later, when we got clear of the land.

"Weidemann had hired the steam schooner *Port Angeles* to tow us as far as Coos Bay and cast us loose at the heads for a local tug to take us in. It being summer time, he decided to chance the trip up the coast with just her 250 tons of standing ballast. Didn't want the expense and the work of taking extra ballast and getting rid of it at Coos Bay. Well, his luck ran out. A summer gale caught us off Cape Arago; it blew up worse and worse. Pretty soon the steam schooner didn't want us hanging on to him. He broke out some signal flags. Marzan got out the code book and found she was signalling: ENGINE BROKEN DOWN—CAST OFF TOWLINE.

"Weidemann didn't like this a little bit; to be out there with a handful of men and not enough ballast to carry proper sail. She wasn't stiff enough to carry the sail to claw off the coast. So Weidemann wasn't about to lose the *Centennial*; he got some flags together just before dark and ran up the hoist: WE WILL CONTINUE TOWING.

"That made the steam schooner skipper mad because he went ahead and, with two good jerks, played hell with us. We were towing on the anchor cable and had devil's claws on it forward of the windlass. This carried away and away went the chain by the run. I ran forward with a lantern under the fo'c's'le head. The chain was roaring out the locker and pretty quick the wildcat began to break up. You couldn't get close to the brakes and it wouldn't have done any good, anyway. There were chunks of iron flying around like shrapnel.

"I found Weidemann beside me. He asked Marzan if this chain was shackled to the other. Because if it was, and the end fetched

Bar ports were the terror of the Pacific coasting trade . . . Here the *C. A. Thayer* lies stranded after the Grays Harbor bar tore away her rudder and deadwood in 1908. She was towed to Cosmopolis, careened and repaired.

up with a jerk, it could take the windlass right off the bed. Neither Marzan nor any of us knew. Weidemann told me to take the men and get ready to make sail if we had to. As luck would have it, the two cables weren't shackled together. The end flew out free. But it wrapped itself around the bobstays, gave a jerk, and next thing we knew the headstays had gone slack.

"We were crippled, and caught on a wild, dark night off what would be a lee shore if the wind hauled much farther. I took the crowd and got a reef in the fore and afters and then there was nothing for it but wait until morning. The gale got worse in the night.

"At daylight, the signal station up there must have seen us because they sent a tug out to get us. But a tremendous sea got up and the tug had to turn back because the bar was breaking too bad. On the third try, the tug got out over the bar. We got her

At night, Nereids danced around the compass . . . A discarded cardboard tube that once contained a lady's girdle made a shade for the schooner's binnacle light.

hawser fast around our foremast. But our troubles were not over, because the *Centennial* took a sheer as she went over the bar and struck bottom twice. It set her to leaking. The tug finally got us in; we anchored inside the jetty. We were all played out but I stayed up to keep steam up in the donkey. Our trouble was a freak gale. There was hail during the night. I scooped up handfuls big as marbles.

"We loaded lumber, and had a new wildcat for the windlass cast in San Francisco and sent up. The question when I joined her had been whether at 21 I could handle the men. There was nothing more said about that. I left with her for Melbourne when we were loaded. That leak we started on the Coos Bay bar plagued the ship all the way to Australia and back. But those old Downeasters took a lot of killing. She was an old ship then —fifty-two years old."

When the port watch turned out at midnight, they found that the doctor had ordered Mr. Dickerhoff to keep in his bunk for a full night's rest. He had been nursing a painful chest bruise after being struck by the spanker boom tackle a couple of days before. He had been keeping his misery to himself. Captain Raynaud had the word passed for the watches not to make the half-hour bells so that the mate could have a sound sleep and all night in.

It was a windless night with the *Thayer* rolling listlessly, and with soft skies broken at the horizon by far-off rain squalls. A dark shape suddenly appeared at the companionway. The mate lumbered painfully out of the after cabin like a bear shuffling out of his den. Hearing the *Minnie A. Caine's* clock strike the cabin bells, the mate insisted on standing his watch. Captain Raynaud protested, but the mate took over the deck. He coughed dispiritedly, even let the standby man make him some coffee. This wasn't like the old *Centennial* man.

Forward the men speculated soberly on the ultimate indignity —a Coast Guard helicopter being sent out—and Mr. Dickerhoff being "rescued," dangling on the end of a string.

In all his lifetime at sea or in the rigging lofts ashore, what episode satisfies him most? Jack Dickerhoff's eyes lit up when that question was put to him, and the lines relaxed around his mouth.

"I guess it's when I was second mate of the *Centennial*—and I was 21."

Chapter VII

Potatoes Down Under

Nobody understands better than a sailing ship man the philosophy that reconciles us to living in the eternal now. Even so, conformity does not always come easily. Faces frequently mirror the sea's moods, reflecting first despair and then elation as the music veers from dismal calm to a soul-stirring breeze.

".... Wednesday, Sept. 25 .. 12 to 4—Vessel hardly making way through water; hauled in taffrail log, 58 miles. ..."

But daylight brought a flicker of promise to dispel the climate of disappointment.

"... 6—Wind freshening from Southeast; vessel making about five knots. ..."

By breakfast time, the men's moods had changed altogether. The starboard watch had left the mate's men a piping legacy that made the schooner's wake bubble away to the northwest. The skies darkened as the morning wore on. There were spits of rain. A Coast Guard plane droned into view from the direction of Point Arena and made low, blasting circles around the walloping ship. Soon he was lost in the rain squalls on the far swing of his wide ocean watch.

Mr. Dickerhoff was a new man now. He mused contentedly as the gnarled genius in his horny fingers spliced a lizard into a neat little strap for the spanker boom tackle. He reckoned the ship would be in fine shape by the time we fetched Australia.

All afternoon, the other watch had practiced tacking her. Six times Captain Raynaud tried to bring the old hooker around. Six times the skipper was unsuccessful. Mr. Dickerhoff lay in his

79

bunk below listening to the rumpus on the monkey poop—waiting, like Thomas E. Dewey, to be drafted. Finally, the watch ran up the white flag. The captain sent for the chief mate. Again the schooner missed stays, trying to bring her head around to the wind. With the sea that was running, the mate switched tactics by jibing. The schooner wore around and went off blithely on the opposite board.

Royal Danish Ballet . . . Second mate Johnnie Gruelund walks on air for a moment; Seaman Gordon Fountain minds the helm.

This baffling behavior in seagoing unhandiness was a lively fo'c's'le topic. As long as the *C. A. Thayer* kept trying to steer "steamboat courses," as long as her recalcitrant bow refused to walk up into the wind's eye, theory continued to feed on her worst foibles.

Years ago, Capt. Ole Lee of San Francisco, who had the *Thayer*

The Old Man . . . Light winds plagued Captain Raynaud most of the way.

on her second Australian voyage, recalled that he had "never once had to wear ship." And when sailing south along the coast, "We sailed steamer courses close in."

Turned stanchions and wooden shutters . . . Old style joiner work provides a period setting for the second mate.

Clearly, this sailing the ship close-hauled, "pinched" hard on the wind, was no part of the schooner's earlier ritual. "We never sailed her close-hauled," Captain Lee remembered, "except when beating into a narrow place." But in Ole Lee's time, the *Thayer* had a gaff-headed spanker. This gave her the sail power aft to swing her up into the wind and around on the other tack.

One of the inexplicable traits of this old schooner—part of the lore gleaned from her heyday—was that she all but steered herself and spun on her keel like a seagoing Pavlova when trimmed down a foot by the head. This was Captain Lee's careful recollection of the hours spent in shifting heavy water casks forward to put the schooner's head down to the trim she liked best for the Australia voyage.

Ole Lee's life in the *C. A. Thayer* perhaps marks one of her more glorious chapters. In September, 1914, the *Thayer* left San Francisco for Grays Harbor and by mid-October was outward-bound for Sydney piled with lumber clear over her deck house and after cabin.

Capt. William Anderson had her on her first deepwater voyage. Ole Lee was mate. The schooner went south to the latitude of San Diego, then stood away to the southwest across the long lonely ocean. The *Thayer* passed east of Christmas Island, then south of Samoa, making her landfall a little north of Newcastle, New South Wales. Her 66 days was a fair "average" passage.

The *Thayer* discharged, towed down to Sydney and loaded copra and hardwood for San Francisco. Homeward-bound, she stood away to the south of New Zealand and arrived off the Golden Gate on the 82nd day. For these long ocean voyages, the *Thayer* carried topsails and set a square sail on the fore to give her an extra lift in the strong, steady-blowing trades.

When the E. K. Wood Lumber Company sold the *C. A. Thayer* in 1912 to Capt. Peter M. Nelson, San Francisco's famous Whitehead Pete put her in the Alaska salmon trade. With the outbreak of War in Europe in August, 1914, the big jump in ocean freight rates offered Pete better fishing in other waters.

Nelson offered Ole Lee the command for another Australian voyage. They settled on terms of $250 a month captain's wages and the privilege of taking his family along. Whitehead Pete swallowed hard. Taking the family was all right, but $250 was unheard-of pay for a schooner captain. Only a month before he died in the winter of 1957, Captain Lee reminisced with the author about his 1918 voyage to Australia, in the *C. A. Thayer*, reliving this happy and profitable interlude of his life in sail.

"The most important thing about a long voyage is that you have plenty of potatoes. I told Whitehead Pete that I wanted the best. I saw to their stowing myself. I dumped them on shelves in the *Thayer's* lazarette and covered them over with slaked lime.

Musings, musings . . . And now and then a spoke or two.

We had fresh potatoes every day from San Francisco to Australia and back to the San Francisco pilot boat."

The keeper of the flower gardens in Union Square never nursed his plants more devotedly than Ole Lee nurtured his Merced spuds deep under the *Thayer's* lumber-clogged poop. Lime-burrowed potatoes was only one of Captain Lee's practical wrinkles in deep-sea victualing. Recollections of the 1914 voyage's sorry provisioning had set his Scandinavian wits to working. As captain of the *C. A. Thayer*, he vowed she would feed better. Instead of stowing potatoes in the old sail locker forward, he stowed four hogsheads of fresh water forward where it could be shifted into the forward tank and pumped directly up to the galley house.

Aft, he stowed salt beef, salt salmon, canned goods and flour. Lee's penchant for good victualing brought the old schooner some fame. And later an alert publicist for the Eagle Milk Company wangled some warm human-interest pictures of Captain and Mrs. Lee's fat-legged cherub who, during the long traverse, was nurtured on canned milk and potatoes preserved in slaked lime.

All this was not in it, of course, with the icebox fare served up by our topnotch amateur sea cook in the *Thayer's* farewell to the sea. Clark Turner was almost a genius. Even so, there was grumbling among the hearty consumers of fresh milk and butter and roast beef. And some disenchanted remarks that there's nothing like salt horse and pea soup to stick to a sailor's ribs, from the quibblers for authenticity, gnawing their way through the schooner's head-high ice box.

On the 1918 Ole Lee voyage, the *Thayer* shipped a crew at San Francisco, then went north to Fort Bragg and loaded "beautiful" redwood lumber. There it blew up such an awful storm one night, all hands had to leave the ship. Chain moorings were streamed to rocks ashore, but the seas in that exposed dog-hole port were broaching clear over the wharf. "If you had steam, you could get clear of the land and ride it out," Captain Lee explained. But sailing vessels had to hold on and hope for the best. "That was almost the last of the *C. A. Thayer.*"

Life at sea was just as interesting to the Lees, and safer, it seemed. The schooner again steered southwest of San Diego on this second voyage "down under," then stood straight across the ocean. Approaching Samoa, around Apia and Tonga, she ran into a field of volcanic lava. As far as the eye could see, there was nothing but lava so that Ole Lee remembered, "It was like sailing over a sandy beach. It gave us a headache to look at it. The mates picked up lava hunks for holystoning the *Thayer's* decks."

For two days the schooner plowed through that weird pumice patch. Whales joined up in schools, curiously eyeing the men walking fore and aft along the deckload. The fishing was good, too; and there was fresh bonita or dolphin to go with the spuds that had forgotten to sprout in the slaked lime.

Great chains kept the redwood deckload from shifting, set fiddle taut with steel turnbuckles, slobbered with grease and tallow to keep boarding seas from rusting the threads. In those days, the master and mates would tend to the loading. The captain worked in the hold seeing that the vessel did not leave port with a crack of daylight unused, getting lumber for beam-filling. In the hold, you load to the ship's sheer. On deck, you load her flat, and ignore the vessel's sheer. Ole Lee remembered the art of lumber schooners to the last.

" 'N there's dancin' 'n fiddlin' of ev'ry kind o' sort, it's a fine place for sailor-men . . . 'N I wish—I wish as I was there . . . "

The *Thayer* made her landfall for Ole Lee on Nobby's Light, near Newcastle, and followed the coast down to Sydney. Lighters discharged her 575,000 of redwood clears in the American lumber ship anchorage of Johnson's Bay. Loading copra for San Francisco, waterfront watchers admired the rake to the jib-boom she flaunted ahead of her bowsprit in those days. If you look carefully now, you can see where the old deckhouse has been lengthened to shelter a one-lung Hercules pumping and hoisting engine. In Ole Lee's time, she worked cargo with a steam donkey that was always secured at sea. She set sail by hand—four sailors, the cook and the donkeyman and the two mates, were all the sea engines Captain Lee could muster on deck.

Gasoline handy-billies were too luxurious for Whitehead Pete's vessels. The *Thayer's* crew bent their backs to iron pump handles. She barely "wept" enough to keep her bilges sweet. Bendixsen ships were known to be as tight as a teacup.

But on this second Australian voyage, the schooner strangely developed a troublesome leak. For 10 days the men pumped. Captain Lee squirmed on his belly through every opening in her

Washboard rhythm . . . Doc Norton catches up on a few days' "dobeying".

lumber-laden innards. Down aft in the dry stores, finally, Lee heard a trickle coming out of the overboard discharge, from the captain's wash basin. He found that the ship's thirsty rats, wanting no part of potatoes preserved in slaked lime, had gnawed a hole in the lead pipe searching for fresh water under the captain's cabin.

Homeward-bound, early in 1919, Captain Lee laid off a track south of New Zealand again. One night, soon after picking up the strong westerlies, the *Thayer* found herself heading straight for the two islands, the "Antipodes," lying in 40 degrees south latitude and about 178 degrees west. There's a narrow passage between them. Blindfolded by darkness and rainsqualls, Captain Lee steered between them unscathed.

This duster was the forerunner of a southerly antarctic gale. While sailing close-reefed, the fore and main throat halyards parted, wrecking the foregaff. The men worked a long splice in the main throat halyards and got the reefed sail on her again.

The crippled schooner rode out the storm. Meanwhile Captain Lee sent up the cargo gaff on the fore. This spar was too heavy and had to be sent down again. The gale had let up and Lee couldn't sleep until he had more pulling power back on the fore. Remembering the old leg-o-mutton spanker the schooner used to set as a storm trysail, the crew rummaged it out and set it on the fore while the officers set to work repairing the splintered gaff.

Splints were fashioned out of 3-inch square hardwood pieces used for chafing gear where the gaff jaws rub against the mast These were fished to the gaff and secured by drilling holes into which some spare boiler tube stoppers were bolted. The fished gear was as strong and light as new. Lee had warm words of praise for the mate, a land carpenter, who drilled and sawed for four days on a deep-sea thesis that was to earn him his citation as an authentic "Chips." And while all this work was going on, so was the schooner, with the help of that leg-o-mutton spanker set at the fore. The foresheet on this Irish get-up had to be led aft through the side chock on the stern.

The *Thayer* made good time as far as Pitcairn Island. There the wind let up and for 30 days the schooner wallowed off this infamous landmark where the mutineers wrecked the *Bounty* and set up their island kingdom. From the Equator, the schooner drove on to San Francisco in 20 days. Off the Mexican coast, a sudden rain squall caught the *Thayer* napping in her summer suit of sails, blowing the fores'l and forestays'l "clear out of the leech." Even as Captain Raynaud, Ole Lee was "sewing all the time." A schooner's sail needles are almost never still.

But it was a voyage to remember, to glow over in retrospect.

Capt. Ole Lee remembered the day outward bound in the north-east trades when the *C. A. Thayer* sailed into an ocean adrift with heavy logs. Plainly a raft, towing down to San Diego, had broken clear of its tug and been swept out into the westward-trending currents and broken up, somewhere along the illusive track, per-haps, that the ill-fated raft *Lehi* had failed to find. There were

In the fo'c's'le . . . Many of the crew kept a daily journal of the *Thayer's* final passage.

logs as far as the men could see in every direction, as endless, seemingly, as the lava sea the schooner had encountered earlier on this second Australia voyage. Captain Lee could only survey the logs, millions of board feet of them, and sigh for want of an empty ship. By the law of the sea, he could have sold all he could carry away, and the floating wealth would have been all his.

These are the moments men remember. The *Thayer* had many that Captain Lee would recall often in later years. He remem-bered trailing astern a triangle made of brass and wood and baited

Fifty miles off shore . . . The *C. A. Thayer* jogs in toward the California coast.

with salt pork which made an exciting way of catching albatross. And the chute he rigged under the mains'l with a leader to the fresh water tank so that there was plenty of it all the time, all the crew ever needed for drinking and to keep the longboat full for bathing. Deckhouse water gets slimy very quickly, but the *Thayer's* canvas-captured rain didn't.

Memories, memories. A wonderful day it was, when the *Thayer* stood in toward the Farallones in 1919 and found the San Francisco pilot boat waiting with six big steaks and a basket of

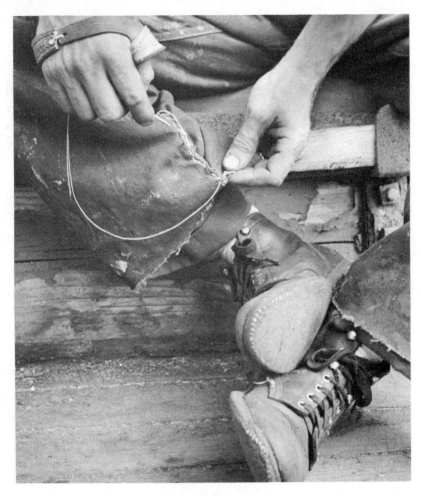

Homeward-bound stitches . . . When a sailor patches his pants, the nearer home, the longer the stitch.

oranges. Best of all, he remembered the son who was eight months old when the schooner left Fort Bragg; and how he used to give him his morning bath in a barrel, and how little George Lee learned to walk aboard the *Thayer*. When Capt. George

Hudson Lee was master of the *Jacob Luckenbach* years later, he could point to the three-master and say, "That's where I found my sea legs."

".... 12 Noon—Lat 39° 13′ North, Long 125° 35′ West. Distance by log 28 miles. 4—Wind and sea increasing; furled outer jib. Barometer 29.76. Vessel laboring moderately in beam sea."

The schooner is flying now, eight, maybe ten knots. Axel clumps aft with a heavy storage battery re-charged and ready for the captain's nocturnal colloquy with the Maritime Museum's Dave Nelson, whose welcoming committee is getting more fidgety by the day.

As darkness descends on the men singing in the waist, the wind is driving the schooner in toward the land. Dead ahead some 60 miles, lies Fort Bragg, where Ole Lee and his family began that satisfying second voyage to Australia 40 years before.

Chapter VIII

The Schooner Comes Home

Capt. Adrian Raynaud came on deck remarking, "The glass is still falling." So were the pots and pans in the galley.

The *C. A. Thayer* was flying now. "Oh, for the life of a sailor!" Mr. Gruelund grinned as he went star-hunting with his sextant in the wild evening twilight.

The watch below and the idlers collected under the taut bulge of the big drumming mains'l. For all of its forty-two patches, the old sail was pulling hard. Yet only this morning Mr. Dickerhoff had snorted, "It fits like a Civil War nightgown."

Gordon Jones bobbed up out of the schooner's fo'c's'le girding on his accordion. At the break of the poop, the mate lorded over his high realm of wind-hard canvas and almost smiled.

The lee scuppers were trailing their toes in the water at every big roll. The voices in the waist let out with the thundering chorus:

> Blow the man down, boys
> Oh, blow the man down.
> Yo, ho, we'll blow the man down.

The young carpenter lunged and swayed and his foot tapped out the tempo of the old sea chantey as though the music in his fists could blow the man down without any help from the roaring half circle around him.

Turner, the cook, joined in the chorus in the waist. Mr. Dickerhoff braced himself against the low trunk of the afterhouse and eyed the dark shadows of the sails swaying across the broken starlight.

The mate had gone north a fortnight early to oversee reeving

93

of the long halyards and to bend sail to the exact old ritual. He had cast a critical eye at the Seattle rigger's work, and had re-tuned the heavy shrouds and stays to his liking. Now he was seeing his handiwork put to the hardest test:

> Three slenderest pinnacles, three sloping spires,
>   Climbing the sky, supported but by strings
> Which whine in the sea wind from all their wires,
>   Yet stand the strain however hard it dings.

Inner jib downhaul.

"Steering east by north magnetic. Barometer 29.70. Rain. Heavy sea."

Drops of rain rolled off Captain Raynaud's sou'wester and made puddles on the chart as he bent over his logbook.

The old schooner drove hard through the night, south by east on a tack that was taking her in toward the coast at Navarro Head.

This treeless, 400-foot cliff is characteristic of the forbidding shoreline these West Coast schooners skirted in storm or fog.

The *C. A. Thayer* drummed east by north on a line of charted soundings showing 1,700 fathoms. And from headland to headland, from Point Arena to Cape Mendocino, this mile-deep ocean marches abruptly up to California's red rock ramparts. For here, the ocean floor scorns any gradual semblance of a 100-fathom curve. From 1,600 fathoms, the bottom eases steeply to 800 fathoms, 200 fathoms, 30 fathoms, then headlong against the cliffs in shooting white walls of spray.

Some ships are built for a life of leisurely sailing along aquamarine coral keys, or lazy south sea island trading. But not these square-beamed West Coast lumber schooners. Now and then, one of them drifted into palm-fringed southern seas in trades that were like going out to pasture. But still more of them headed for ice-strewn Bering Sea for the cod and salmon salteries when their coasting days were over.

Old timers still exult over the *C. A. Thayer's* prodigious "Pay day" in the 1918 Alaska salmon season. The schooner was just home from a successful Australian voyage under Capt. Ole Lee when Whitehead Pete Nelson decided to use her that summer in his salmon business again.

Capt. Oscar Jacobson was hired to sail her up to Squaw Creek where Whitehead Pete had a station right across the river from Naknek. Captain Jacobson's brother, Victor, went mate. The *Thayer* was the "mother" ship, transporting the fishermen, the grub and the stores north for the season's work.

The schooner fitted out at Oakland Creek. A temporary platform was built in the fore part of the hold with bunks to sleep the thirty fishermen.

Gus Carlson, a retired Oakland fisherman, remembers the *Thayer's* 1918 salmon trip because it was the biggest pay-day of his life. And it staked him to a house and bride.

Coming up through Unimak Pass, the *Thayer* got hung up in the ice setting down out of Bering Sea. Ice worked havoc with the cannery ships. That was the year the old Downeaster, *Tacoma*, was lost. The *Emily F. Whitney* got into trouble. The *Star of France* was set ashore by the ice.

Some of Gus Carlson's old shipmates were in the *Tacoma*. Later on, he heard the story from other Oland Island Swedes who

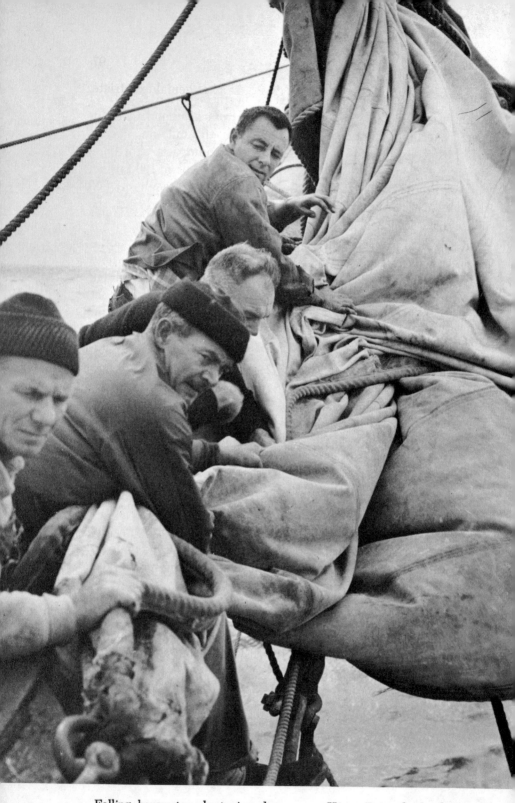

Falling barometer—shortening down . . . Harry Dring leads the men muzzling the jib.

used to gather in the East Street saloon run by a genial expatriate known as "Oland's King."

The *Tacoma* tried to anchor in the drifting ice, trusting two anchors to withstand the tide-impelled glacier. But her anchor chains cut through the hawsepipes, slicing her open like fine wire through a slab of cheese.

The *Thayer* did not fight the ice. When the fresh water was used up, the crew bailed up pools on the melting floes, and refilled the schooner's casks.

After a week, the floe broke up, and the *Thayer* sailed north with Capt. Jacobson perched in the schooner's fore crosstrees shouting orders like a veteran polar ice pilot, "Starboard a little, starboard there! Steady!"

The schooner's grub got monotonous, Carlson remembered, "Salt salmon and potatoes one day, and potatoes and salt salmon the next day just for a change." After Unimak Pass, the crowd got hooks down and found the cod would bite at anything, would even take the bare hooks as fast as they were lowered. The bored fishermen fed on flaky fresh cod and boiled potatoes, dredged in sizzling pork scraps. Good living!

Still, it was a fine passage. Less than a month out of San Francisco, Whitehead Pete had his men all ashore fitting out the boats that had laid all winter upside down on the beach at Squaw Creek. Everybody moved ashore except the schooner's donkeyman.

Pete's saltery used 20 salmon boats, two men to a boat, fishing day and night. Oars and sails propelled the heavy gill netters. It was all man power—there was a law against using motor boats in the salmon fisheries.

The men fished until their scaly cargoes all but sank the boats. When rain squalls came up in the night, the two-man crews crawled under the spray cloth in the bow, warmed their hands over the Primus oil stove, and slept a little.

Whitehead Pete stalked the beach at Squaw Creek, cheering the men on. "That's the way to fish boys. Keep 'em coming." Gus Carlson remembered how happy Pete wanted everybody to be—fishing. Boat crews streamed nets from an anchor, carried the bitter end ashore and dragged it up the beach until they couldn't drag the slithering, silver haul another inch. Salmon were tossed onto the wharf and tallied. There was a crew to clean them. The fish were tossed into big tanks. Every day the station tender, a gas boat, collected the harvest and carried it down to Pete's salt station in the hole-in-the-wall creek near Naknek.

The men got $35 a month wages and so much extra per fish. That exciting summer of 1918, the men had it made in twenty-eight days. Gus Carlson's stake in the *C. A. Thayer's* round trip voyage from San Francisco, from May to August, was $1,800.

Whitehead Pete Nelson made a big stake out of the *C. A. Thayer's* voyage that summer, too. Everybody celebrated. Pete was from Oland Island, too. They were all friends together. This made for better relations than the big canneries that hired mixed droves of Italians, Scandinavians and Chinese.

Pete Nelson was a shrewd businessman. His office was in his hat. When he wasn't fishing, he was selling. He closed deals in saloons, on street corners, on the church steps, traveling the wintery half of the year. From Oakland to Chicago and New York, wholesale dealers said, "Here comes Pete Nelson, the salt salmon man."

Whitehead Pete liked to talk about the 1918 year, the year of the "big stake" when the *C. A. Thayer* loaded 6,000 barrels at Naknek homeward bound, and sent out another 6,000 barrels of that whopping twenty-day catch down to Seattle in the old Bath full-rigger, the *St. Nicholas.*

Thursday, Sept. 26. The twelfth day. The four-to-eight watch tumbled out in oilskins. The mate was waiting for them at the hatch coaming. "Keep your eyes peeled for land," he warned. "We don't want to bring her about before daylight. Neither do we want to get hung up on a lee shore."

The *Thayer* was doing seven knots on the log, close-hauled. Should he shorten down, or stand on until daylight when the men could see what they were doing? The rain slashed at Mr. Dickerhoff's upturned face. The next gust might send the old sails flying out of their bolt ropes. Steady as she goes!

The tension aft was shattered by a sudden bell. John Davies' yell came floating aft with it: "Light, dead ahead." Big John

Hove-to in a southeast gale . . . The *C. A. Thayer* struck heavy weather off Cape Cabrillo.

ran aft. The mate was halfway down the waist to meet him. "All Hands!"

Cape Cabrillo lay dead ahead in the howling black maelstrom. The fo'c's'le was in a turmoil. "We're on a lee shore!" Men, half believing, tumbled out sleepy-eyed, timing the violent pitch of the ship as they struggled into storm clothes.

As fast as the men emerged out of the fo'c's'le, the mate sent them running to the belayed gear.

Down came the head sails and the fore, the main, the spanker. The gear whipped smoking off the pins. A raging green ocean widened around the schooner in the first wild streak of morning twilight.

"You there, Kortum, tend that gaff downhaul! Axel, give him a hand! Take a turn when she rolls!" The mate led the charge. "All right, Dring, you and Riehl slack away—handsomely!" The mate was wearing the ship offshore. She fell away into the trough, rolling deeper than ever before.

Another monstrous roll to leeward, bigger than all the rest, set off a splintering explosion of crockery in the galley and a roar of anguish as Turner tried to rescue eighteen men's breakfast. The big agate coffee pot was banging wildly against the fiddles.

Here is how those wild moments seemed to Seaman Karl Kortum in his day-to-day journal. "Rain flew in sheets off the top of the deckhouse. Through it I saw half a dozen men whipped across the deck when a turn got loose and the gaff took charge. It had a look of comedy and pain. Several were flung against the hatch combing. Blood streamed from Gordon Fountain's smashed hand.

"Dickerhoff charged in to get turns around the gaff and snub it down to the rail. I heard him sing out and saw the swinging gaff end nearly clout the only indispensable man on board.

"I worked numbly—cold, wet, and seemingly strengthless. This was a lee shore, right out of the books; we were working to save the schooner—and our necks. There is a strange, temporary evaluation of spirit under these circumstances; it is unquestionably what impelled men to broach the liquor aboard a ship in distress. I suppose leadership makes it easier to bear or dispel it. I pushed myself to get on with the work at hand, which was reefing the fores'l.

"Harry said seriously that it would be a shame to lose the schooner now. We tugged at the deadly heavy canvas, finding the reef band and one by one threaded through the reef points.

"Taciturnly, Dickerhoff asked if I realized now why he had kept Fountain and me busy in Seattle, making sixty reef points and assembling them in neat bundles."

A gray streak of land opened through the wrack and rain. A big steamer, deckloaded with lumber, was suddenly our companion in the gale. He was nearly stopped, with green water cascading over the fo'c's'le head. Maybe the steamer's captain thought he was dreaming dreams, seeing the apparition of a nineteenth-century windjammer clawing off a lee shore.

Half-seeing the steamer, the men stormed the fores'l, fisting in the heavy canvas and tying in the reef points one by one. The crowd reefed the mizzen. Suddenly some one said, "See, we're on the other tack."

The shore was under our stern. The schooner's motion became less violent now as she lay hove-to under reefed fores'l and spanker. With her untended wheel lashed hard over in beckets, the schooner rode the crests like a seabird—her head tucked under her wing.

The mains'l blew out again . . . Sail-mending went on between squalls; aft by the mizzen mast a man pumps ship.

Now every blast of the gale only made the schooner fore-reach a little further out to the safety of the open ocean.

". . . . 10 a.m.—Full gale from the south east. Vessel hove to laying South West by South. Barometer 29.65. In the middle of storm . . . . 12 noon—Latitude 39° 27' North, Longitude 124° 12' West. Distance by log 71 miles. Sea and wind beginning to moderate."

On deck, the men sewed patches in the tired old mains'l with the rain pelting down hard.

". . . 4 p.m.—Heavy rain, sea. Shook out all reef points, set all sails by hand. Donkey engine would not start. Vessel laboring hard all this day. Steering by the wind on the starboard tack. Barometer 29.70."

A weird note of suspended time hangs over the laboring schooner. Slowly, as in a Greek tragedy, the coincidence in the plot approaches full circle. The stage was the same expanse of troubled gray water. The central play was the same schooner.

The yellowing pages of the Tacoma *Daily Ledger*, January 14, 1912, tell the story: "EIGHT AT MERCY OF SEA—SCHOONER *THAYER* SENDS CALL FOR AID"

"Lumber carrier from Grays Harbor in sinking condition off Humboldt Bar," cried the *Ledger* tersely. "One woman on board. Tug which started to relief of vessel is unable to cross bar in dense fog. Ship is waterlogged. Steamer *President* reports the wreck by wireless to Eureka and proceeds on her way to San Francisco."

Reporting under a Eureka dateline, the *Ledger* said:

"A crew of seven men and a woman are in grave danger aboard the American schooner *C. A. Thayer* which lies tonight twenty miles off Humboldt Bar, leaking badly and momentarily in danger of sinking. Owing to the roughness of the Humboldt Bar, the schooner's calls for help so far have not been answered, as a heavy fog combined with a rising sea makes it extremely perilous for a tug to try to venture out. The schooner is too far distant for life savers to render aid.

"The first intimation of the *Thayer's* plight reached Eureka at 7 p.m. when a wireless message was received from the steamer *President* reporting that the schooner was in distress and asking that a tug to sent to her assistance. The *President*, evidently believing that aid would be dispatched to the vessel, proceeded on her course. The Table Bluff government station reported at 9 p.m. that the *President* had steamed off and that, with her departure, all communication with the sinking schooner had been lost. The last message given by the *President* was that the *Thayer* was settling low in the water and was in urgent need of help.

"A tug was prepared to go to the schooner's relief at the first news of the disaster, but it was found impossible to cross the bar while the fog held. The little boat is standing in readiness, to make a dash for the open sea the instant the mists clear away.

"The *Thayer* left Grays Harbor nine days ago, bound for San Pedro with 400,000 feet of lumber. It is judged by the meager wireless reports that the vessel struck one of the gales which have been raging off the coast recently and that the heavy buffeting of the sea opened her seams. The trouble grew rapidly worse and the vessel soon became unnavigable. Unless the tug is able to clear the bar tonight, it will proceed to sea with the first streaks of daylight."

The next day's *Ledger* said:

"The schooner *C. A. Thayer*, waterlogged and leaking badly, and with her pumps out of commission, was picked up by the steamer *J. B. Stetson* and is being towed south according to a wireless message received late tonight by the government station at Table Bluff."

Two days later, the *Ledger* carried the finale:

"The schooner *C. A. Thayer*, which was sighted in distress off Eureka by the steamer *President* Saturday night and which, for a time, was feared lost, was towed into San Francisco tonight by the steam schooner *J. B. Stetson*.

"The *Thayer* was sunk deep in the water owing to the opening of her seams and the failure of her pumps, but her cargo of lumber was intact, and Captain Fred Scott, his wife and seven crew men were unharmed.

"The *Thayer* left Grays Harbor on January fifth and two days later began taking water faster than the pumps could discharge it. The hand pumps failed shortly and the steam pump had to be stopped because nearly all the fresh water on board had been consumed. A tug spent all day Sunday searching for the *Thayer* but, owing to the thick fog, did not sight her.

"Sunday night the *Stetson* was signaled and took the *Thayer* in tow after putting four men aboard to repair and help man the pumps. The *Thayer* will be towed to Oakland and her cargo discharged."

This time fate was more relenting.

On the thirteenth day, the wind fell away to a flat calm and the old question came back to haunt the captain. With enough full rations for only another day, should he get on the *Thayer's* radio telephone and ask the Coast Guard to send out some food?

After the storm . . . Flotsam from the waterlogged fo'c's'le spread to dry on the main hatch.

It is the captain's time for decision. He stands perplexed between two centuries. The schooner lolls on an empty sea, once again, a few sea birds mewing forlornly around her. Captain Raynaud reflects on a scene seemingly unrelated to time or place. Yet the men forward are prisoners of the Twentieth Century. Into this illusion of time, they have each brought a little ration of it.

Certainly time is a relative thing, and the time on the men's wristwatches has no bearing on that meted out by the bells of the *Minnie A. Caine's* clock in the after cabin. That concept of time belongs to an era we call history. This which marks the present is more demanding, more unforgiving, more pressing than anything that ever figured in Capt. Ole Lee's transpacific reckoning. Or the time that belonged to Whitehead Pete Nelson's seasonal quests for Alaska salmon; or in Fisherman Gus Nelson's gloating over how he had his Bering Sea "stake" made in twenty days.

Today's meaning of time is inexorably synonymous with pressure. And, very plainly, the *Thayer* is caught up in its relentless new meaning.

Axel must get back to his job with the telephone company in San Francisco. John Davies' leave is running out in Alameda. Doctor Norton's practice in Tacoma is weighing heavily on his thoughts. And for many of the *Thayer's* crew, earnings have stopped altogether.

Had not the *Thayer* sailed from Grays Harbor to San Francisco in four days the year that city was leveled by earthquake and fire? On this voyage, we are victualed for fourteen days, but who would have guessed it would take over ten with the North Pacific equinox breathing down Captain Raynaud's seamed neck?

The skipper braced himself in the cabin armchair under the swinging lantern, slowly turning over his thoughts out loud. "I have these volunteer people to think about." He spoke deliberately. "I would not want to risk a man's job just to be stubborn or prideful."

This was the old *Edward Sewall* man talking, Capt. Richard Quick's former second mate, reaching for righteous judgments in the slow earnest way he had learned at the right hand of Bath's old Lion-Hearted Richard. A man not wanting to be "stubborn or prideful."

The radio watch on the *Blunt's Reef* Lightship picked up the schooner's signal and relayed it into the Coast Guard station at Humboldt's Bay, asking for emergency stores and to be towed the rest of the way to San Francisco.

". . 4 to 8—Both watches tacked ship to port tack. Dead calm all the watch. No steering way. Vessel pitching and rolling in big swells. Sails slamming. Vessel barely answers helm. Cloudy with patches of light fog."

The Coast Guard radioed they would be at the ship at 10:15 in the night.

The age of sail was passing, passing—the great galaxy of white-winged ships.

The tug arrives . . . The *Avoyel's* lights grope for the windless schooner.

> Each with her grace, her glory
> Her memory of old song, or comrade's story.
> Still in my mind, the image of life's need,
> Beauty in hardest action, beauty indeed.

The lookout struck two bells. "Light off the port bow!" The captain lit off a flare and climbed laboriously into the mizzen shrouds, holding the red fire aloft in his fist.

The Coast Guard's running lights came into view, and the deep, rhythmic rumble of her main engines throbbed across the dark swells. Two fierce range lights stabbed the darkness, groped through the schooner's rigging, then held her rolling silhouette in their eerie blue grasp.

The big, pulsing shadow drifted broad abeam and stopped. A voice in the dark said, "Stand by to lower."

"Away, the boat!"

A long leaping swell surged up beside the *Avoyel*, felt for the motor whaleboat's lithe keel and lifted it free of the falls.

Heavy fog had set in around the two ships. The whaleboat closed with the schooner's sea ladder. In the boat, a boy's voice chirped, "Give us a line and we'll pass up these stores."

Two canvas bags as big as a steam shovel's bucket lay the midship thwarts. Flaked neatly under them were the long leading folds of an eight-inch nylon hawser.

"Mind this bag," the boyish voice warned. "The eggs are right on top." The shadowy figures in the schooner's waist inched the heavy bags up the rolling side in the midnight scene that was like a rendezvous with Christmas Eve.

"Our captain says to please put plenty of chafing gear on your turns," the coxswain called out as the men walked the big nylon hawser forward to the bow chocks.

The whaleboat sped away as silently as she had come. The range lights switched off and a voice out in the darkness said, "All engines ahead one third."

It was 10:15 by the *Minnie A. Caine* clock in the cabin skylight. Out in the fog, the *Avoyel* took up a strain on the new nylon hawser.

This was the thirteenth day from the *Swiftsure* Lightship. For the last time, the sails were stowed in the *C. A. Thayer*, the last of the West Coast schooners.

The men standing there in the darkness looked up wearily at an old windjammer's bare masts and saw an era come to its close.

EPILOGUE

Between the spinning news-burst of the second Sputnik—and poor Mutnik—West Coast readers may have stolen a glance or two at local headlines about a project that seems to cement a hand-hold on the slow-motion past. Meaning efforts made by a volunteer company of sailing-ship admirers in bringing the last native lumber schooner, the three-master *C. A. Thayer* to rest in the State's maritime historical monument at San Francisco.

With the Soviets' second Sputnik navigating outer space at the rate of umpteen-thousand miles an hour, the slow-motion impact of the schooner that came a thousand miles from Seattle to San Francisco in fourteen days was all the more startling, be it all but in reverse.

Even by more down-to-earth comparisons, there were startling contrasts in the *C: A. Thayer's* passage to posterity. The day before the schooner sailed, I was winging west from London in Pan American World Airways' new Arctic clipper that ties the Old World to the New West in 18-hour flights.

We had dipped through fog over Frobisher, but, finding the Baffin Land field shut in, swooped back above the morning sky wrack and flew to the alternate field at Sondrestrom on the Greenland west coast to refuel. Pan Am's skipper said that as soon as there are a couple more radar beacons on the Frobisher approaches, polar travelers will be able to pass up the Greenland alternate. Still, Greenland was an extra thrill, and a stark and icy contrast to the schooner voyage that lay only a few hours ahead.

These old schooners exacted a hard discipline in work and patience. Feeling the lift of the old wooden decks and seeing the dark shadows of sails making slow arcs across the stars awakened memories of a voyage long ago in the Downeast three-mast schooner, *Frank Brainerd*.

108

In through the Golden Gate.

There were five of us: Capt. Will Tyler of Tennants Harbor, Maine; Mate Jim Adkins of Yarmouth, Nova Scotia; cook, Charlie Crocker of Machias, Maine; seaman John Pedersen of Copenhagen and myself. I was a nimble 19. The other's ages ranged from 55 to 79. We pumped two hours in every four-hour watch all the way from Weymouth to Wolfeville down in Nova Scotia.

Living was elemental. When we were weather-bound seventeen days at one stretch and out of galley fuel, we rowed across to the *Ella Clifton*, a two-mast schooner from Orland, and warmed our conscience by "borrowing" a ton of coke from her Perth Amboy cargo. And when our little iron firepot in the fo'c's'le ran out of firewood, John and I "borrowed" oakum out of the bosun's locker and kept warm at Merrit Ober's expense. Mr. Ober ran the general store over at Northeast Harbor on Mt. Desert Island, and dabbled in schooners. And, as they say Downeast, we figured he was "good for it."

In those days, the crew worked cargo; so we rigged a Spanish burton off the main gaff, hired an old white horse, and landed the 200-pound sacks of phosphate ourselves. That was before the CIO. There was no justice in it for the tired old white horse either. On Sunday, I hired him out with a buggy and drove out to the Gaspereau with a taffy-haired girl from Acadia College to see the herrings run the falls.

A berth was ready for her.

The schooner is home . . . She joins the *Balclutha* to symbolize the past.
In the distance, the newest Matson liner heads out to sea.

I remember beating in past Cape Blow-Me-Down in midnight
snow squalls, thinking Will Tyler must be a praying man, tacking
in and out among so many high black spruce shadows and missing
all of them. The next morning's landlocked scene confirmed it.
We were anchored off a Christmas-card village. A little white
steeple was giving out angels' music, and farmers were walking
their women and children across the glistening snow.

This was only twenty-eight years before the Soviets' second
Sputnik lit out into space,—and the *C. A. Thayer* came home to
San Francisco.

APPENDIX

VESSELS BUILT BY H. D. BENDIXSEN ON HUMBOLDT BAY, CALIFORNIA

(Based on a listing in *Log Chips*, September, 1949.)

Built at Eureka

Year	Name	Gross tonnage	Type	Fractional share owned by Bendixsen.
1869	FAIRY QUEEN	99	Two-mast schooner for Sacramento River.	
1870	UNDINE	144	Two-mast centerboard schooner.	
1871	SILVA	18	Humboldt Bay steamer.	
1872	MARION	48	Two-mast schooner for Tahiti.	
1872	LILLIE JONES	38	Humboldt Bay steamer.	
1872	MARY	49	Two-mast schooner for Tahiti.	
1872	ELVENIA	148	Two-mast lumber schooner.	
1872	STELLA	49	Two-mast schooner for Tahiti.	
1872	ATALANTA	49	Two-mast schooner for Tahiti.	
1873	AURORA	193	Two-mast lumber schooner.	
1873	SILVA	41	1871 vessel lengthened.	
1873	JOHN McCULLOUGH	72	Two-mast lumber schooner.	
1874	VENUS	80	Two-mast schooner for Tahiti.	
1874	GOLDEN GATE	97	Two-mast lumber schooner.	
1874	HUMBOLDT	138	Two-mast lumber schooner.	
1874	O. S. FOWLER	35	Two-mast schooner.	
1874	LOVELY	80	Two-mast schooner for Tahiti.	
1875	VINE	50	Two-mast schooner for Tahiti.	
1875	VARAO	68	Two-mast schooner for Tahiti.	

Built at Fairhaven

Year	Name	Gross tonnage	Type	Fractional share owned by Bendixsen.
1875	LA GIRONDE	80	Two-mast schooner for Tahiti.	
1875	MARY SWANN	143	Two-mast lumber schooner.	
1875	PALOMA	223	Half-brig for Tahiti.	
1875	J. G. WALL	98	Two-mast lumber schooner.	
1875	LOTTIE COLLINS	69	Two-mast lumber schooner.	
1875	LAURA PIKE	145	Two-mast lumber schooner.	1/8
1875	JOHN N. INGALLS	95	Two-mast lumber schooner.	
1875	PAULINE COLLINS	69	Two-mast lumber schooner.	
1875	ALBERT & EDWARD	96	Two-mast lumber schooner.	

1875	MARY ANN	76	Steam tug (rebuilt).	
1876	MARTHA W. TUFT	173	Two-mast lumber schooner.	
1876	MARY BUHNE	147	Two-mast lumber schooner.	
1876	EXCELSIOR	348	Three-mast lumber schooner.	
1876	LIZZIE MADISON	131	Two-mast lumber schooner.	
1876	MAXIM	117	Two-mast lumber schooner.	
1876	ABBIE	146	Two-mast lumber schooner.	
1876	SAN BUENAVEN-TURA	180	Two-mast lumber schooner.	
1876	CHRISTINA STEF-FENS	70	Two-mast lumber schooner.	
1876	DAVID & ETTIE	69	Two-mast lumber schooner.	1/8
1876	GUSSIE KLOSE	94	Two-mast lumber schooner.	
1876	MORNING STAR	99	Two-mast lumber schooner.	
1877	COMPEER	347	Three-mast lumber schooner.	
1877	ALBERT & EDWARD	96	1875 vessel repaired.	
1878	ALTA	104	Humboldt Bay stern-wheeler.	
1878	GEORGIE R. HIGGINS (with Thomas H. Peterson)	96	Two-mast lumber schooner.	
1878	ORION (with Thomas H. Peterson)	117	Two-mast lumber schooner.	
1878	HINAARI	65	Two-mast schooner for Tahiti.	
1879	DAISY ROWE	122	Two-mast lumber schooner.	
1879	EDWARD PARKE	147	Two-mast schooner (rebuilt).	
1880	IDA McKAY	187	Three-mast lumber schooner.	
1881	VEGA	245	Three-mast lumber schooner.	
1881	BERTHA DOLBEER	242	Three-mast lumber schooner.	
1881	CHARLES HANSON	192	Two-mast lumber schooner.	
1882	FALCON	205	Three-mast lumber schooner.	1/16
1882	MABEL GRAY	205	Three-mast lumber schooner.	
1882	NEPTUNE	184	Two-mast lumber schooner.	
1883	WESTERN HOME	128	Two-mast schooner (rebuilt).	
1883	CITY OF PAPEETE	389	Barkentine; Tahiti packet.	
1883	JESSIE MINOR	261	Three-mast lumber schooner.	
1883	VOLANT	172	Three-mast lumber schooner.	
1884	BERTIE MINOR	272	Three-mast lumber schooner.	
1884	OCCIDENTAL	209	Three-mast lumber schooner.	1/16
1886	FORTUNA	145	Two-mast lumber schooner.	1/8
1887	BARBARA		Two-mast lumber schooner.	
1887	ESTHER BUHNE	287	Three-mast baldheader.	1/16
1887	WM. F. WITZEMANN	487	Four-mast lumber schooner.	
1888	ALLEN A.	342	Three-mast baldheader.	
1888	GLENDALE	296	Three-mast baldheader.	
1888	NORTH FORK	322	Steam schooner.	
1889	CHARLES E. FALK	298	Three-mast baldheader.	1/8
1889	H. C. WRIGHT	290	Three-mast lumber schooner.	1/16

Year	Name	Tonnage	Description	Fraction
1890	G. W.WATSON	452	Three-mast baldheader.	1/16
1890	SEQUOIA	341	Three-mast baldheader.	1/16
1890	AZALEA	344	Three-mast baldheader.	1/16
1890	SADIE	310	Three-mast baldheader.	
1890	LUCY	309	Three-mast baldheader.	
1891	ROY SOMERS	314	Three-mast baldheader.	1/8
1891	R. W. BARTLETT	521	Four-mast lumber schooner.	1/8
1891	CZARINA	230	Three-mast baldheader.	
1892	CHARLES R. WILSON	345	Three-mast baldheader.	1/8
1892	LOUISE	346	Three-mast baldheader.	
1892	HILO	644	Barkentine.	1/16
1892	OTTILIE FJORD	261	Three-mast baldheader.	1/16
1892	JANE L. STANFORD	970	Four-mast barkentine.	1/16
1892	O. M. KELLOGG	393	Three-mast baldheader.	1/16
1894	DORA BLUHM	330	Three-mast schooner (rebuilt).	
1895	C. A. THAYER	453	Three-mast baldheader.	1/4
1895	MAWEEMA	453	Three-mast baldheader.	1/8
1896	ALBERT MEYER	459	Three-mast baldheader.	3/16
1896	METHA NELSON	460	Three-mast lumber schooner.	7/32
1896	DEFENDER	446	Four-mast baldheader.	9/32
1896	HUMBOLDT	1075	Coasting steamer.	
1896	ALLIANCE	679	Steam schooner.	
1897	WAWONA	468	Three-mast baldheader.	5/24
1897	MILDRED	464	Three-mast baldheader.	7/32
1897	HUENEME	341	Steam schooner.	1/16
1898	H. D. BENDIXSEN	641	Four-mast lumber schooner.	5/32
1898	A. M. BAXTER	516	Four-mast lumber schooner.	7/32
1898	JAMES H. BRUCE	533	Four-mast lumber schooner.	1/4
1898	FULTON	380	Steam schooner.	1/16
1899	WILLIAM CARSON	890	Four-mast barkentine.	1/16
1899	JAMES ROLPH	586	Four-mast lumber schooner.	1/16
1899	DESPATCH	698	Steam schooner.	1/16
1899	S. T. ALEXANDER	779	Four-mast lumber schooner.	
1900	STANLEY	355	Three-mast lumber schooner.	
1900	SANTA PAULA	650	Oil tank barge; four masts.	
1900	NOME CITY	939	Steam schooner.	1/32
1900	IAQUA	712	Steam schooner.	1/32
1900	JOHN PALMER	1187	Four-mast barkentine.	
1900	IRENE	772	Four-mast lumber schooner.	1/16
1901	ALVENA	772	Four-mast lumber schooner.	1/16

Index